The Chemistry of Organometallic Compounds

The Chemistry of

ORGANOMETALLIC COMPOUNDS

THE MAIN GROUP ELEMENTS

JOHN J. EISCH

The Catholic University of America

The Macmillan Company / *New York*
Collier-Macmillan Limited / *London*

FIRST PRINTING

Library of Congress catalog card number: 67–18886

The Macmillan Company, New York
Collier-Macmillan Canada, Ltd., Toronto, Ontario

Printed in the United States of America

This book is dedicated to my teacher

Henry Gilman

whose legendary, pioneering researches on organometallic compounds have enriched the science of chemistry and whose boundless curiosity and enthusiasm have inspired his many students to carry on the quest.

Preface

The expanding importance of organometallic compounds, both in organic synthesis and mechanism studies on the one hand, and in preparing metal derivatives of unusual structure and valence state on the other hand, commands the attention of every chemist. The time-honored antipathy between workers in the different fields of chemistry has dissolved rapidly. Organic researchers now realize that much intriguing chemistry can be won by foraging in the bailiwick of the inorganic chemist. The latter, in turn, finds organic ligands to be most useful frameworks in the study of metal coordination compounds. Due to their mutual appreciation of metal chemistry both types of researchers are beginning to view each other in a kinder light.

This book evolved from a series of lectures on organometallic compounds delivered to graduate students primarily interested in organic chemistry. It was found desirable to devote class time to a consideration of trends in structure, physical properties, and chemical reactivity in the light of existing electronic theory. Illustrative examples were chosen from a wide variety of organometallic types, in order to stress the unifying principles of the subject. To portray the ferment of current research, selected descriptive topics were discussed in conjunction with pertinent readings in specific reviews and in original research reports. Although several existing books treat the individual chemistry of organometallic types in a systematic and excellent fashion (see the research bibliography given on p. 164), a need was felt for a concise, correlative presentation of the principles of organometallic chemistry, suitable as an introduction to research. This brief book is an attempt to fill that gap.

vii

The vast area of transition metal-organometallic π-complexes, excepting some comparisons with classical organometallics and a brief treatment of ferrocenes, has been omitted from this book. The behavior of σ-bonded organometallics of transition metals has many similarities with main group metal alkyls, and thus these metal alkyls can be discussed profitably together. Where the present state of organometallic chemistry (January, 1967) does not permit a conclusive electronic formulation of certain structures and reaction mechanisms, this book attempts to assess the contributing factors and to formulate viewpoints consonant with present knowledge and amenable to future research. Let us hope that in this manner the student can be brought to the frontiers of organometallic chemistry in an intellectually satisfying fashion and, further, be stimulated to attack the many remaining problems in structure and chemical behavior.

Since "I am part of all that I have met," I owe an incalculable debt of gratitude to my professors and colleagues in organometallic chemistry, especially Henry Gilman, Karl Ziegler, and Georg Wittig. Special appreciation also is extended to Raymond Dessy, whose critical reading of the entire manuscript enhanced its accuracy and clarity.

J. J. E.

Contents

ix

The Chemistry of Organometallic Compounds

ONE

Scope of Organometallic Chemistry

Nature of Organometallic Compounds

Organometallic chemistry is the study of those compounds containing direct carbon-metal linkages. Inasmuch as any organometallic compound (R_mM) can be considered as the metal salt of the corresponding pseudoacidic organic compound (R-H), the number of possible organometallic derivatives of any given organic compound would equal at least the number of different carbon hydrogen bonds present. Thus, toluene can form four isomeric organometallic compounds with any given metal. Inclusion of various types of organometallic π-complexes increases the number possible [for example, the sandwich complex, $(C_6H_6)_2Cr$]. Since over a million organic compounds have been characterized, the number of possible organometallic derivatives is clearly legion. As a further complication, the higher valence state and the solvating properties of certain metals multiply the number of discrete organometallic derivatives obtainable from just one given organic and one metal moiety. For example, methylaluminum derivatives can range from the simple type (identical groups), trimethylaluminum (I), to the mixed types (dissimilar groups), dimethylaluminum chloride (II) and methylaluminum dichloride (III):

$$(CH_3)_3Al \qquad\qquad (CH_3)_2AlCl \qquad\qquad CH_3AlCl_2$$

I II III

1

In addition, each of the compounds I–III can form isolable solvates with ethers and other Lewis bases and can also form auto-complexes with itself. The trimethylaluminum actually exists as a dimer[1] and the methylaluminum chlorides have the possibility of existing as isomeric bridging structures (IIIa–IIIc)[2]:

$$
\underset{\text{CH}_3}{\overset{\text{Cl}}{\diagdown}}\text{Al}\underset{\text{Cl}}{\overset{\text{Cl}}{\diagup}}\text{Al}\underset{\text{CH}_3}{\overset{\text{Cl}}{\diagdown}}
\qquad
\underset{\text{Cl}}{\overset{\text{Cl}}{\diagdown}}\text{Al}\underset{\text{Cl}}{\overset{\text{CH}_3}{\diagup}}\text{Al}\underset{\text{CH}_3}{\overset{\text{Cl}}{\diagdown}}
\qquad
\underset{\text{CH}_3}{\overset{\text{Cl}}{\diagdown}}\text{Al}\underset{\text{Cl}}{\overset{\text{Cl}}{\diagup}}\text{Al}\underset{\text{Cl}}{\overset{\text{CH}_3}{\diagdown}}
$$

chloro "bridge"	methyl "bridge"	chloro "bridge"
cis		*trans*
IIIa	IIIb	IIIc

Often it is profitable to consider that the nature of an alkyl group $R = C_nH_{2n+1}$ shall encompass even those cases where $n = 0$ and hence include metal hydrides. In structure and properties there is much to strengthen the close relationship between metal alkyls and metal hydrides.

As to the nature of the metal partner in organometallic compounds, the definition of a metal element is difficult to formulate with great precision. Consequently, the only useful approach appears to be an operational definition, based upon discernible similarities among element-organic compounds.[3] Chemical behavior, such as rapid oxidation (1–1), facile cleavage by protic agents (1–2), and complex formation (1–3), seems to be common to most organometallic compounds:

$$
\begin{array}{ll}
\quad\quad\quad\overset{\text{O}_2}{\nearrow}\quad\text{R}-\text{O}-\text{M} & (1\text{–}1)\\
\text{R}-\text{M}\xrightarrow{\ \text{H}-\text{S}\ }\text{RH}+\text{M}-\text{S} & (1\text{–}2)\\
\quad\quad\quad\underset{:\text{B}}{\searrow}\quad\text{R}-\text{M}\leftarrow:\text{B} & (1\text{–}3)
\end{array}
$$

From a combination of such behavior patterns and modern theory of atomic and molecular structure, two electronic characteristics appear to accompany such chemical reactivity. First, since the carbon-element bond involves the union of carbon with a less electronegative element, the resulting electronic density is higher about carbon than about the metal partner, $\overset{\delta-}{\text{C}}-\overset{\delta+}{\text{M}}$. Second, the metal centers in such organic compounds display valence unsaturation and hence can combine with Lewis bases (B:), such as amines, ethers, and halide ions (R—M←:B). The Lewis acidity of the organometallic compounds can be ascribed to the availability of low-lying unfilled atomic orbitals on the metal center. The absence of such atomic orbitals in the organic deriva-

[1] P. H. Lewis and R. E. Rundle, *J. Chem. Phys.*, **21**, 986 (1953).
[2] Cf. (a) C. P. Van der Kelen and M. A. Herman, *Bull. Soc. Chim. Belges*, **65**, 362 (1956); (b) R. E. Glick and A. Z. Zwickel, *J. Inorg. Nucl. Chem.*, **16**, 151 (1960).
[3] J. Eisch and H. Gilman in *Advances in Inorganic Chemistry and Radiochemistry*, Vol. II (H. J. Emeleus and A. G. Sharpe, eds.), Academic, New York, 1960, pp. 61–103.

tives of metalloids and nonmetals (Groups IVA–VIIA) and the lessened polarity of the carbon-element bonds involved rationalize their inertness toward Lewis bases and toward the oxidation of their carbon-element bond. Thus, for the purposes of organometallic chemistry it is useful to define *organometallic compounds* in electronic terms; that is, as compounds containing anionic carbon or carbon σ-bonded to a more electropositive element which has available low-lying *p*-orbitals in the combined state. This electronic statement would limit the term "organometallic compound" to those carbon derivatives of Groups I–III and to any organic derivative of a transition metal containing an ionic or σ-carbon-metal bond ($CH_3^-Na^+$, $[(CH_3)_2Be]_x$, $(CH_3)_2Si$, and $(CH_3)_3TiCl$). The common electronic feature would be the availability of *np*-orbitals on the metal atom.

Organic derivatives of the metalloids (silicon, phosphorus, iodine, etc., whose electronegativity or $X_E < X_C$) do not have all the typical properties of ordinary organometallic compounds, but their behavior is reminiscent of such types.[4] Their lower reactivity is apparently a reflection of the lessened C—E polarity and the absence of *np*-orbitals of low energy. However, here the role of somewhat higher energy *d*- and *f*-orbitals seems to be prominent in determining the chemical reactivity and stereochemistry of C—E bond cleavages. It appears appropriate to term compounds containing carbon σ-bonded to an element having only a slightly less electronegativity and having available *d*- and *f*-orbitals as *organometalloidal compounds* [CH_3SiCl_3, $(C_6H_5)_3As$, $(C_6H_5)_3PbCH—CH_2$, and $(C_6H_5)_3GeH$]. They will be considered in this book principally to bring out their slight resemblance to typical organometallic compounds.

In addition, a vast class of organic derivatives of metals has come into prospect, in which an unsaturated organic group is bonded to a transition metal, in whole or in principal part, by electronic interactions involving the organic moiety's π-electronic orbitals and the metal's *d*-hybrid orbitals. Organic ligands, typified by olefins (IV), acetylenes (V), cyclopentadienyl

IV   V   VI   VII

---

[4] C. Eaborn, *Organosilicon Compounds*, Academic, New York, 1960. Since X_{si} and the actual electronegativities of other metalloids are sensitive to the nature of the ligands to which they are attached, some mixed types, such as $RMCl_{m-1}$, seem able to coordinate with Lewis bases (p. 91).

(VII), benzene, cycloheptatrienyl (VII), unsaturated heterocycles, and poly-olefins (VI), are usually disposed geometrically about the metal center so that the π-electronic orbitals can overlap with unoccupied metal d-orbitals.[5] The resulting μ-bonding does not receive adequate explanation merely by such envisaged Lewis base (organic ligand)-Lewis acid (metal center) inter-actions, for the donation of electrons from filled metal d-orbitals to un-occupied, antibonding ligand orbitals is of comparable importance. With this understanding in mind, these compounds may be classified formally as *organometallic π-complexes*. This classification distinct from ordinary organometallic compounds can be justified both on a structural and on a behavioral basis. In such complexes π-bonding between several carbon atoms and one metal center is a pervading characteristic, and hence the concept of an isolated carbon-metal bond loses its meaning. Moreover, organometallic π-complexes respond to oxidizing agents, solvolytic agents, and Lewis bases in a rather distinct way and hence should be treated separately.

Finally, it might be observed that just as organometalloids can be con-sidered as muted analogs of organometallics, wherein the metal center is exchanged for a metalloid atom, there is an excellent and noteworthy parallel between organometallic compounds (C—M) and metal derivatives of carbon's congeners.[6] Thus, the behavior of silylmetallic, germylmetallic, and stannyl-metallic compounds, such as triphenylsilyllithium $[(C_6H_5)_3SiLi]$, toward organic systems is strongly remindful of organometallic compounds [cf. $(C_6H_5)_3CLi]$. Nevertheless, such systems do not contain carbon-metal bonds. It appears proper to classify such systems as *organoidal-metallic compounds*. To prevent the abundance of all metal derivatives of inorganic acids from

$$Na{-}O{-}\overset{\overset{\displaystyle O}{\|}}{C}{-}CH_3$$

dominating this class ($NaNH_2$, $NaOH$, $Na{-}O{-}\overset{\overset{O}{\|}}{C}{-}CH_3$, etc.), one might concentrate on carbon analogs whose electronegativity and electronic struc-ture is not too divergent from that of carbon. Naturally, however, this class could accommodate such borderline organometallic derivatives as enol salts, metal sulfides, amides, and other metal derivatives of weak organic acids, where a metal bond involving oxygen, nitrogen, or sulfur is a prominent feature.

Significance of Organometallic Chemistry

The number of permutations permissible in organometallic structures probably surpasses that encountered in any other branch of chemistry, and

[5] (a) G. Guy and B. L. Shaw in *Advances in Inorganic Chemistry and Radiochemistry*, Vol. IV (H. J. Emeleus and A. G. Sharpe, eds.), Academic, New York, 1962, pp. 77–131; (b) E. O. Fischer and H. P. Fritz, *ibid.*, Vol. I, pp. 56–115.
[6] D. Wittenberg and H. Gilman, *Quart. Rev. (London)*, **13**, 116 (1959).

thus the number of possible organometallic derivatives is almost unimaginable. As with the historical reasons which prompted a separate study of organic compounds themselves, the foregoing considerations argue for the prudence of giving organometallic compounds individual attention.

However, the importance of a class of compounds is not necessarily related to the number of possible derivatives. Consequently, other factors underlying the tremendous importance and growth of organometallic chemistry should be stressed. Prime among these is the esteem that organometallic reagents have earned in the field of synthetic organic chemistry. The reactivity of the carbon-metal bond forms a convenient site in an organic molecule for many facile and important reactions. The chemical versatility of Grignard reagents, organolithium compounds, and metal hydrides of Group III has become so extensive in organic chemistry as to require individual treatises for their discussion. Indeed, fundamental organometallic chemistry now represents one of the most fruitful contributors of novel synthetic methods and mechanistic studies to the discipline of organic chemistry. It would appear that these "unnatural" products have usurped the role of natural products as the primogenitor of modern organic chemistry.

Second, since the current theory of valence and structure represents the chemist's grasp of his physical world, the repeated contributions of organometallic compounds to the advance of valence theory have clearly resulted in a constantly expanding horizon of "allowable" chemical formulas. The electron-deficient, bridging structure of metal alkyls, the sandwich configuration of ferrocene types, the metal adducts of conjugated organic compounds, the interesting metal valence states of certain organometallic compounds, and, in general, the behavior of carbon-metal bonds have necessitated drastic revision in previous concepts of structure and bonding in compounds. Thereby, however, a much deeper insight has been gained into the nature of bonding forces between atoms. Indeed, the more such bonding is studied, the more prominent become such nuances in valence theory as polarity, available orbitals, polarizability, and steric fit. The diversity of organometallic structure has always played a prominent role in revealing the chameleonic character of current valence theory.

Third, a common interest in organometallic compounds has exerted a mediating influence between inorganic chemistry and organic chemistry. The traditional and proudly maintained distinction between these two fields found its historical source in the lack of any abiding, common interest, but was perpetuated past its usefulness by a general air of provincial superiority. However, the distinction loses its value in organometallic chemistry, since knowledge of both inorganic and organic chemical principles is called into play in organometallic research. There will still be organic chemists who are primarily interested in the behavior of the organic moiety R in R—M, as determined by the valence capabilities of the metal, M, as indeed inorganic chemists will hope to gain insight into the nature of M, as conditioned by its organic ligands, R. Nevertheless, a fruitful rapport has now come into being and chemistry as a whole cannot but profit greatly from this interdisciplinary research in organometallic chemistry.

Historical Development

The child is the father of the man, and the origin and development of organometallic chemistry have foreshadowed the significant roles which this field continues to play in present-day chemistry. Even at its inception the study of organometallic compounds mediated between the diverging fields of organic and inorganic chemistry. The researches of Bunsen and Frankland were motivated by the desire to isolate complex radicals, or element imitators, as a culmination of the type theory of Dumas and Liebig. In isolating the supposed cacodyl radical, $(CH_3)_2As$ [actually, $(CH_3)_2As—As(CH_3)_2$], Bunsen (1842) felt he had achieved the proof for the independent existence of radicals.[7] In so doing, he was also the first to obtain and manipulate pure organo-metalloids. Frankland's attempt (1849) to accomplish the presumably success-ful isolation of radicals for the simple alkyl radical case resulted, at first, in failure (Eq. 1–4). Very few "failures" in the field of chemistry, however, have been as significant and as fruitful. For not only did his researches with alkyl iodides and metallic zinc lead to the first isolation of a pure organometallic compound, but these metal alkyls and his perceptive mind resulted in Frank-land's lucid and pioneering concept of an element's combining capacity (valence). By the use of zinc alkyls, the alkyl derivatives of a variety of elements were synthesized. Now the number of alkyl groups with which zinc, mercury,

$$2R + ZnI_2 \quad \xleftarrow{\;\;/\!\!/\;\;} \quad 2R—I + Zn \quad \xrightarrow{\hspace{1cm}} \quad R_2Zn + ZnI \qquad (1\text{--}4)$$

tin, antimony, arsenic, and non-metallic elements combined caused Frankland to conclude that "no matter what the character of the uniting atoms may be (alkyl, halide, hydrogen, etc.) the combining power of the attracting element, if I may be allowed the term, is always satisfied by the same number of these atoms."[8] Thus, in principle, these organometallic compounds reconciled the attractive features of Berzelius' dualistic theory of inorganic compounds (electrostatic attraction between combining partners) with those of Dumas' theory of types for organic chemistry (combining tendencies between atoms or

---

[7] R. Bunsen, *Ann.*, **42**, 14 (1842).
[8] E. Frankland, *Ann.*, **71**, 171 (1849); **85**, 347 (1853); **95**, 28 (1855).

radicals resulting in certain fundamental classes of substances). Although not yet given in fundamental terms, Frankland's theory stressed an inherent (though variable in certain cases) combining capacity for elements, regardless of whether the compounds were organic or inorganic in nature.

The synthesis of metal alkyls by subsequent investigators became an integral part of characterizing newly discovered metallic elements, for such volatile derivatives allowed the valence number and accurate atomic weight of the metal to be determined. Thus Winkler's studies with ekasilicon (germanium) uncovered a tetraethyl derivative whose density and boiling point had been predicted by Mendeleev by interpolations of his periodic table.[9] In addition, in the hands of Paneth and coworkers, the same metal alkyls served successfully as the source of the elusive alkyl free radicals sought by Frankland.[10] More recently, the highly associated character of certain alkyls of Groups I–III has been interpreted in terms of bridging structures, whose existence has inspired the concept of electron-deficient bonding.[11] Finally, the isolation of alkali metal alkyls, whose structure consists of metal cation-alkyl anion pairing, would warm Berzelius' heart, since it is an organic example of his famous dualistic theory.

The introduction of organometallic π-complexes actually anteceded that of organometallics and organometalloids, in that Zeise isolated an ethylene "solvate" of platinum, $KPtCl_3 \cdot C_2H_4 \cdot H_2O$, in 1827.[12] However, for the most part, this area lay dormant for over 120 years, until Kealy and Pauson tried unsuccessfully to couple cyclopentadienyl radicals and thereby discovered ferrocene, bis(cyclopentadienyl) iron.[13] The phenomenal growth of this field in barely a decade's time has now given it a breadth that makes it no weak handmaid of organometallic chemistry, but indeed a vigorous copartner. In presenting the structural chemist with extraordinary geometrical insights into chemical bonding (sandwich and bridging features), these compounds thereby have allowed theoreticians to gain a more profound understanding of the role of d-orbitals in determining molecular structure and properties. The accelerated advances possible in this area undoubtedly owe a large debt to the early flourishing of transition metal carbonyl chemistry.[14]

It seems also fitting to comment briefly on the contribution of organoidalmetallic compounds to valence theory, as this area appears destined to develop very rapidly in the future. Because of their relationship to organometallics, silylmetallic compounds presently appear to be receiving the most attention

[9] C. Winkler, *J. Prakt. Chem.*, **36**, 177 (1887).

[10] F. A. Paneth and H. Hofeditz, *Ber.*, **62**, 1335 (1929).

[11] R. E. Rundle, *J. Phys. Chem.*, **61**, 45 (1957).

[12] W. C. Zeise, *Pogg. Ann.*, **9**, 632 (1827); **21**, 497 (1831).

[13] T. J. Kealy and P. L. Pauson, *Nature*, **168**, 1039 (1951).

[14] J. Chatt, P. L. Pauson, and L. M. Venanzi in *Organometallic Chemistry* (H. Zeiss, ed.), Reinhold, New York, 1960, p. 460.

and will be the focus of our remarks. Although the first organosilylmetallic compound, $(C_6H_5)_3SiLi$, was reported by Kraus and Eatough in 1933,[15] some twenty years passed before the field received intensive examination. Work by Gilman[6] and by Benkeser[16] has uncovered a host of interesting and striking organic reactions of such systems, but more insight into the structural and electronic properties of such compounds will have to await the isolation of the pure compounds. Judging by the frequent contrasts their behavior makes with that of typical organometallics, one can expect with some assurance that organoidal-metallics still have much to reveal.

The second principal impetus to research in organometallic chemistry has been the synthetic utility of these compounds. On the one hand, metal alkyls long have served for the preparation of other metal alkyls by means of trans-alkylation (Eq. 1–5):

$$M—R + M'X \rightarrow M'—R + MX \tag{1–5}$$

Consequently, the scope of such synthetic procedures is limited by the alkyl-ating ability of the metal alkyl, R—M. Moreover, each class of metal deriva-tives is found to possess its own peculiar suitability in diverse organometallic syntheses. Thus it is understandable that each new preparative technique for different R—M derivatives has made new organometallic types available. Pacesetting preparative discoveries include:

    a. Zeise's[12] olefin-platinum salt complex by direct interaction, 1827;

    b. Frankland's[8] discovery of zinc alkyls, 1849;

    c. Dimroth's[17] studies on aromatic mercuration, 1898;

    d. Grignard's[18] direct preparation of organomagnesium halides, 1900;

    e. Schlenk's[19] researches on organoalkali compounds, 1914;

    f. Ziegler's[20] direct preparation of lithium alkyls, 1930;

    g. the preparation of ferrocene[13] as the first sandwich organometallic π-complex; and

    h. Ziegler's[21] preparation of aluminum alkyls via olefin and hydride, 1955.

On the other hand, organometallic procedures play an indispensable role in the precise synthesis of organic molecules. In addition to the utilization of the foregoing list of metal alkyls in organic synthesis, the following synthetic advances may be cited:

[15] C. A. Kraus and H. Eatough, *J. Am. Chem. Soc.*, **55**, 5008 (1933).

[16] R. A. Benkeser and R. G. Severson, *J. Am. Chem. Soc.*, **73**, 1424 (1951).

[17] O. Dimroth, *Ber.*, **31**, 2154 (1898).

[18] V. Grignard, *Compt. Rend.*, **130**, 1322 (1900).

[19] W. Schlenk, J. Appenrodt, A. Michael, and A. Thal, *Ber.*, **47**, 473 (1914).

[20] K. Ziegler and H. Colonius, *Ann.*, **479**, 135 (1930).

[21] K. Ziegler, H. G. Gellert, K. Zosel, W. Lehmkuhl, and W. Pfohl, *Angew. Chem.*, **67**, 424 (1955); *Ann.*, **629**, 1 (1960).

a. Gilman's[22] nuclear metalation of aromatic hydrocarbons with organo-lithium reagents;

b. Gilman[23] and Wittig's[24] halogen-lithium interconversion reaction (aryllithium reagents from aryl halides and butyllithium), 1938;

c. Wittig's[25] methylenation of carbonyl compounds with methylene-triphenylphosphoranes;

d. H. C. Brown's[26] hydroboration of olefins with boron hydrides, 1956; and

e. Methylenation agents of the M—CH$_2$—X type for organic compounds.[27]

The third factor responsible for bringing organometallic chemistry to its present prominence is the widespread industrial interest in these compounds. Despite their sensitivity to solvolysis and oxidation, their flammable and poisonous character, and the expense of the necessary starting materials, such organometallic compounds as those of aluminum, lithium, magnesium, mercury, and cobalt are now made on a fairly large scale. Now not only are such compounds used stoichiometrically in industrial chemistry but, more interestingly, they can be used as catalysts or promoters in many organic oligomerization and polymerization processes. Principal among the latter are:

a. Roelen's[28] oxo process whereby olefins react with hydrogen and carbon monoxide under agency of Co$_2$(CO)$_8$;

b. Reppe's[29] acetylene oligomerization and condensation reaction employing cuprous acetylide and certain organometallic π-complexes; and

c. Ziegler's[30] oligomerization and polymerization of various alkenes and alkadienes by means of aluminum alkyl-transition metal salt combinations.

Nomenclature

The generally accepted manner of naming organometallic or organo-metalloidal compounds is that of adding the name of the organic groups as

[22] H. Gilman and R. V. Young, *J. Am. Chem. Soc.*, **56**, 1415 (1934); H. Gilman and J. W. Morton, Jr., in *Organic Reactions*, Vol. VIII (R. Adams, ed.), Wiley, New York, 1954, pp. 258–304.

[23] H. Gilman and A. L. Jacoby, *J. Org. Chem.*, **3**, 108 (1938); H. Gilman, W. Langham, and A. L. Jacoby, *J. Am. Chem. Soc.*, **61**, 106 (1939).

[24] G. Wittig, U. Pockels, and H. Dröge, *Ber.*, **71**, 1903 (1938).

[25] G. Wittig, *Angew. Chem.*, **68**, 505 (1956).

[26] H. C. Brown and B. C. Subba Rao, *J. Am. Chem. Soc.*, **78**, 5694 (1956); *J. Org. Chem.*, **22**, 1136 (1957); H. C. Brown, *Hydroboration*, Benjamin, New York, 1962.

[27] (a) H. E. Simmons and R. D. Smith, *J. Am. Chem. Soc.*, **81**, 4256 (1959); (b) G. Wittig and K. Schwarzenbach, *Ann.*, **650**, 1 (1961); (c) G. Wittig and F. Wingler, *Ann.*, **656**, 18 (1962); (d) H. Hoberg, *ibid*, **656**, 1, 15 (1962).

[28] O. Roelen, U.S. Pat. 2,327,066 (Aug., 1944); *C.A.*, **38**, 550 (1944).

[29] W. Reppe et al., *Ann.*, **560**, 1 (1948); **582**, 1 (1953).

[30] K. Ziegler, E. Holzkamp, H. Breil, and H. Martin, *Angew. Chem.*, **67**, 426 (1955).

prefixes to the name of the metal. In addition, if more than one R group is attached, the appropriate prefix (di-, tri-, or with complex groups, bis, tris, etc.) is attached to the foregoing. For dissimilar groups joined to the metal, the compound is named by citing such groups in alphabetical order. If some other negative group, such as H, X, OOCR, OR, or NR_2, is attached to the metal, the name of this group, ending in *ide*, is placed after the metal's name as a separate word. Alternatively, one may wish to treat such negative groups as prefixes to the compound's name. In this treatment, then, the prefix ending in "o" is allied alphabetically with the other R groups (for example, hydrido, chloro, nitrido, oxo, etc.). The degree of association (dimer, hexamer, polymer, etc.) may be indicated thereupon. Finally, complexation with neutral Lewis bases is expressed by giving the name and number of ether (etherate), amine (amine complex), or similar solvent units allied with the organometallic, if known. Again, such discrete associated or solvated molecules may be named as coordination molecules. The following examples will clarify the rules for such neutral systems:

a. $[(CH_3)_3Al]_2$ is trimethylaluminum dimer or di-μ-methyltetramethyl-dialuminum;

b.

$$C_6H_5\diagdown \qquad \diagup C_6H_5$$
$$C{=}C$$
$$H \diagup \qquad \diagdown Al(C_6H_5)_2$$
$$\uparrow$$
$$O(C_2H_5)_2$$

is diphenyl-*cis*-stibenylaluminum ethyl etherate;

c. $(CF_3)_3Sb \cdot C_5H_5N$ is tris(trifluoromethyl) antimony pyridine complex or tris(trifluoromethyl) (pyridine) antimony;

d. C_2H_5BeH is ethylberyllium hydride or ethylhydridoberyllium;

e. $(CH_3)_2SnCl_2$ is dimethyltin dichloride or dichlorodimethyltin.

In certain cases the metal root is modified in naming metal alkyls; this is especially true with organometalloids. Thus, the roots borane, silane, germane, phosphine, arsine, and stibine, are used preferably, and even alane (aluminum), gallane (gallium), stannane (tin), plumbane (lead), and bismuthane are encountered occasionally. Indeed, in compounds where two or more metal centers are present the alkyl derivatives are often named with these roots, the number of metal atoms in the molecule being indicated by a prefix. For example, $(C_6H_5)_2SnH_2$ is diphenylstannane, $(CH_3)_3Si{-}Si(C_6H_5)_3$ is 1,1,1-trimethyl-2,2,2-triphenyldisilane, and $CH_3BH_2 \cdot BH_3$ is methyldiborane.

In complex systems where it may be desirable to subordinate the metal center in naming the compound, the metal group may be treated as a prefix by changing the *um*, *y*, or *c* ending to *o* or by adding *io* to certain names. Thus, one speaks of $Na(CH_2)_n$ as a sodioalkyl group and $(CH_3)ClSb$ as the chloro(methyl) antimonio group. The mono- and di-sodium adducts of benzene would thus be sodiohydrobenzene and disodiodihydrobenzene, respectively. Alternatively, monovalent radicals are derived from arsine (arsino), stibine (stibino), bismuthine (bismuthino), silane (silyl), germane (germyl), stannane (stannyl), and plumbane (plumbyl). Thus, $(C_6H_5)_3$-GeCH$_2$COOH would be triphenylgermanioacetic acid or triphenylgermyl-acetic acid. For organometallic anions the final *io* of the metal is changed to *ate* and the oxidation number of the metal may then be indicated parenthetically as a Roman numeral. Thus $[Zn(C_6H_5)_3]^-$ is triphenyl-zincate(II), and $[AlH(C_2H_5)_3]^-$ is triethylhydridoaluminate(III). In a complementary fashion, organometallic cations are named in the usual way but the oxidation number is indicated parenthetically by a Roman numeral. For example, $(CH_3)_3HAs^+$ is hydridotrimethylarsenic(V).

Other more specialized styles of naming are treated in the text and in forthcoming reports.[31]

Perspective of the Present Treatment

Since the scope of organometallic chemistry is extraordinarily broad and hence the volume of research literature astonishingly large, no comprehensive survey of the field can be accommodated in a reasonable length. Many excellent monographs on general and special aspects of organometallic chemistry give detailed accounts of the preparation and properties of individual compounds. The present treatment strives to stress the discernible principles of this field and to point out those areas of research in which exploration is now taking place. Since some focal point is mandatory in a concise treatment, the emphasis will be upon the organic behavior of the group R in different R—M compounds and upon the reactivity of such organometallics toward organic substrates. As insights into the structural and electronic nature of such systems are indispensable for an intelligent understanding of organometallic reactions, the discussion will also draw heavily on the fruits of physical and inorganic chemical research. The modern organic chemist is already deeply appreciative of the unique response of various organic substrates toward organometallic reagents. It only remains for this monograph to point out the many unexplored stereochemical, electronic, and mechanistic areas of organometallic chemistry. Let us hope that the fascination with the uncommon chemistry involved helps the organic chemist to overcome his scruples about going beyond the traditional precincts of his field.

---

[31] Cf. (a) IUPAC 1957 report, Nomenclature of Inorganic Chemistry, *J. Am. Chem. Soc.*, **82**, 5523 (1960); (b) Nomenclature of Organic Chemistry, *ibid.*, p. 5545; (c) IUPAC 1966 report, Tentative Rules for Nomenclature of Organometallic Compounds, kindly made available to the author by the chairman, Dr. W. C. Fernelius, Koppers Company, Pittsburgh, Pa.

An examination of present trends supports the contention that many of the individual metals will spawn unique and fruitful branches of organic chemistry all of their own. This should have a subordinating effect on the time-honored organic chemistries of hydrogen, oxygen, and nitrogen. The present vigor noted in the organic chemistry of ferrocenes and silanes surely will be felt soon in other areas. Problems of synthesis, valence, structure, stereochemistry, and chemical reactivity undoubtedly will continue to make fresh and interesting demands on the research chemist.

TWO

Behavior of Metals Toward Organic Systems

Principles of Metal-Organic Substrate Interactions

The interaction of metals with organic substrates is most basic both to the preparation of organometallics and to many significant reactions in organic chemistry. Hence, it is fitting to consider this topic first in order to outline the character of metals and to stress those factors governing their incorporation into organic systems.

For the present purpose, a metal M may be considered an element which combines with an organic system R—Z by a whole or partial electron loss. In general, such interactions can take the form of adduction (Eq. 2–1), cleavage (Eqs. 2–2 and 2–3), or displacement (Eqs. 2–4 and 2–5) reactions:

$$\text{biphenyl} + 2\text{Li} \xrightarrow{\text{THF}} 2\text{Li}^+ \text{(reduced biphenyl dianion)} \qquad (2\text{–}1)$$

$$2\text{CH}_3\text{CH}_2\text{Br} + 2\text{Mg} \xrightarrow{\text{ether}} (\text{CH}_3\text{CH}_2)_2\text{Mg} + \text{MgBr}_2 \qquad (2\text{–}2)$$

$$\text{C}_6\text{H}_5\text{—}\overset{\overset{\text{CH}_3}{|}}{\underset{\underset{\text{CH}_3}{|}}{\text{C}}}\text{—O—CH}_3 + 2\text{K} \longrightarrow \text{C}_6\text{H}_5\overset{\overset{\text{CH}_3}{|}}{\underset{\underset{\text{CH}_3}{|}}{\overset{\ominus}{\text{C}}}}\text{K}^+ + \text{K}^+\overset{\ominus}{\text{O}}\text{CH}_3 \qquad (2\text{–}3)$$

$$2\text{C}_6\text{H}_5\text{C}\equiv\text{C—H} + 2\text{Na} \xrightarrow{\text{liq. NH}_3} 2\text{C}_6\text{H}_5\text{C}\equiv\text{C}^{\ominus}\text{Na}^+ + \text{H}_2 \qquad (2\text{–}4)$$

13

$$\text{⬠} + Fe \xrightarrow[300°]{} (C_5H_5)_2Fe \tag{2-5}$$

To gain insight into the factors promoting such reactions, it is profitable first to consider metal addition reactions. Once this process is understood in broad outline, then cleavage and displacement reactions may be treated as corollaries of such a primary step.

Formation of metal adducts bears a close similarity to metal solution tendencies in aqueous systems. Indeed the Born-Haber treatment of redox potentials can be carried over to the formal redox reaction that occurs in metal-organic substrate interactions[1]:

$$M_s + R\text{—}Z \xrightarrow{-P} M^+_{sol.}[R\text{—}Z]^-_{sol.} \tag{2-6}$$

The more electropositive M_s is and the more electron-attracting $R\text{—}Z$ is, the greater the solution potential of the solid metal M_s. A Born-Haber treatment of the free energy contributions to the solution potential P can be formulated as follows:

$$M_s \xrightarrow{S_1} M_g \xrightarrow{I} M^+_g \xrightarrow{-H_1} M^+_{sol.}$$
$$\downarrow e^- \qquad\qquad\qquad \searrow^{-A} M^+[R\overset{\bullet}{-}Z]^-_{sol.} \tag{2-7}$$
$$R\text{—}Z_s \xrightarrow{S_2} R\text{—}Z_g \xrightarrow{E} R\overset{\bullet}{-}Z^-_g \xrightarrow{-H_2} R\overset{\bullet}{-}Z^-_{sol.}$$

The subscripts denote changes of state of the reactants from solids (s) to individual gaseous units (g) to dissolved or solvated components ($sol.$). The individual hypothetical factors leading to metal solution and adduction with $R\text{—}Z$ are the sublimation energies (S_1, S_2), the first ionization potential of the (monovalent) metal (I), the electron affinity of the organic substrate (E), the energies of solvation of the charged species (H_1, H_2) and the association energy for ionic aggregation in solution (A, being especially important for solvents of low dielectric constant). Thus the solution potential, $-P$ (decrease in free energy for a spontaneous process) can be equated to an equivalent path:

$$-P = S_1 + S_2 + I + E - H_1 - H_2 - A \tag{2-8}$$

Experimental evaluation of P in a stepwise fashion would demand entropy data, in addition to experimentally available enthalpy data, in order to determine individual free energy contributions to P. Since such data are not

---

[1] F. A. Cotton and G. Wilkinson, *Advanced Inorganic Chemistry*, Wiley (Interscience), New York, 1962, pp. 41–42.

easily obtainable, assessments of the important terms can only be done in a semiquantitative fashion. However, existing thermodynamic data prove most helpful in understanding metal-organic substrate interactions (Table 2–1).

TABLE 2–1

Certain Thermodynamic Data for the Alkali Metals

(Values are in units of kcal/g-atom)

Metal	I	$-H_1$ (in H_2O)	S_1
Li	124.4	121.3	36.44
Na	118.5	95.2	25.95
K	100.0	75.0	21.52
Rb	96.1	69.1	20.50
Cs	89.7	61.2	18.83

First, the tenacious crystalline structure of metals, in contrast with the molecular, volatile character of most organic compounds, means in general that $S_1 \gg S_2$. Second, the ionization potential I of the metal will decrease as the electronegativity decreases, cesium (or francium) being in this sense the most reactive. The converse process, the electron affinity E of the organic substrate, will depend upon the unsaturation (delocalization factor) and the electronegative substituents (inductive factor) present in R—Z. The structural features of the latter can cause wide variations in E. (Electronic treatment of this aspect is given below under the discussion of bond cleavage.) Third, the solvation energies ascribed to M^+ and $[R \dot{-} Z]^-$ will usually pertain to aprotic solvents such as ethers and tertiary amines, and hence the Lewis basic character of the latter means specific solvent interaction preferentially with M^+. Therefore $-H_1 > -H_2$. Only in metastable systems as the solution of metals in protic solvents, such as alcohols, ammonia, and primary and secondary amines, would solvation of the anionic $[R \dot{-} Z]^-$ by hydrogen bonding be expected to be important. Indeed, the rapid chemical reduction of organic systems in these latter solvents seems to reflect how easily such anion solvates collapse to reduction products:

$$[R \dot{-} Z]^- \cdots H \cdots O—R' \rightarrow H[R \dot{-} Z] + {}^-O—R' \tag{2–9}$$

Fourth, the relatively low dielectric constant of organic reaction solvents (diethyl ether, 4.34; tetrahydrofuran, 7.58; trimethylamine, 2.42; versus water, 80.4) means that ion pairing will be extensive, even in moderately dilute solutions.

Once one has considered the factors critical in determining the ease of metal adduction, the further complication of metal solution with subsequent cleavage ($Z = X$, OR', SR') or displacement ($Z = H$, M') of R—Z can be treated:

$$M + R\text{—}Z \longrightarrow M^+[R \dot{-} Z]^- \xrightarrow{M} M\text{—}R + M\text{—}Z \qquad (2\text{--}10)$$

In certain metal-organic substrate interactions such metal adducts can be shown experimentally to be intermediates in the formation of cleavage products. Nevertheless, whether such intermediates be formed in every case or not, they can be postulated in a Born-Haber treatment, since overall thermodynamic parameters are independent of the route chosen to reach the products. Consequently, the following Born-Haber cycle for the potential $-P$ of a cleavage reaction may be formulated:

$$
\begin{array}{l}
2M_s \xrightarrow{\; 2S_1 \;} 2M_g \xrightarrow{\; 2I \;} 2M_g^+ \xrightarrow{\qquad -2H_1 \qquad} 2M_{sol.}^+ \\[2em]
\qquad\qquad\qquad\quad \Big\downarrow {\scriptstyle 2e^-} \qquad\qquad\qquad\qquad\qquad \Big\downarrow \\[1em]
\qquad\qquad\qquad\qquad\qquad\qquad R_g^- \xrightarrow{\,-H_2\,} R_{sol.}^- \xrightarrow{\,-A_1\,} M^+R_{sol.}^- \\[1.5em]
R\text{—}Z_s \xrightarrow{\; S_2 \;} R\text{—}Z_g \xrightarrow{\; E_1 + E_2 \;} R\text{—}Z_g^{--} \xrightarrow{\; D \;} + \qquad\qquad (2\text{--}11) \\[1.5em]
\qquad\qquad\qquad\qquad\qquad\qquad Z_g^- \xrightarrow{\,-H_3\,} Z_{sol.}^- \xrightarrow{\,-A_2\,} M^+Z_{sol.}^-
\end{array}
$$

$$-P = 2S_1 + S_2 + 2I + E_1 + E_2 + D - 2H_1 - H_2 - H_3 - A_1 - A_2$$

Although additional metal sublimation energy ($2S_1$), first (E_1) and second (E_2) electron affinities, solvation energy ($-H_2, -H_3$), and association energies ($-A_1, -A_2$) are introduced, the noteworthy new factor is the dissociation energy D of the C—Z bond in the dianion intermediate. If one assumes the importance of such intermediates, either as solution species or adsorbed complexes on the metal surface, then the behavior of many organic substrates toward metals can be systematized. In order to connect these thermodynamic considerations with kinetic factors, it could be postulated either that the rate of adduct formation (electron transfer) or the rate of decomposition (anion ejection) of R—Z^{--} determines the overall rate. From these hypotheses it then becomes understandable why more electropositive metals (Na vs. K or Rb or Cs) are more powerful bond-cleaving agents, why more donor solvents (diethyl ether vs. tetrahydrofuran; diethyl ether vs. trialkylamines) facilitate such cleavage reactions, and why various metals activators (mercury, copper, iodine, and alkyl halides) are utilized. All these phenomena can be related to the acceleration of the rate of electron transfer from the metal to the organic substrate. In a complementary sense, the more readily R—Z accepts electrons, the more readily cleavage seems to occur. Assuming the rate of ejection of Z^- from $R—Z^{--}$ to be rate-determining, the following electronic factors can be cited. First, the presence of conjugated unsaturation in R favors the addition of electrons from alkali metals; indeed, the greater the conjugation, the more readily such metal adducts appear to be formed. Thus, although benzene (Z = H) forms no stable sodium or potassium metal adduct in 1,2-dimethoxyethane at room temperature, naphthalene forms only a 1:1 adduct (radical anion), and anthracene may also yield a 2:1 adduct.[2] Second, with a given R group the more electron-withdrawing Z is $(-I, +T)$ the more readily the system R—Z may pick up electrons. Thus, with benzene (R = phenyl and Z=H) no metal adduct can be detected at 20°C, but with benzonitrile[3] or nitrobenzene[4] ($Z = C\equiv N$ or NO_2) radical anions have been formed readily and completely characterized. Third, certain organometallic and organometalloidal systems (Z = M) possess C—Z bonds which are polarized negatively toward carbon by the inductive effect $(+I)$. However, the possibility of $p\pi—p\pi$ or $p\pi—d\pi$[5] interactions between the unsaturation of R and the available p- or d-orbitals of Z = M give an opposite $-T$ or electron-withdrawing effect to Z. This seems to explain why triarylboranes,[6] triphenylaluminum,[7] phenyl-[8] and vinylsilanes,[9] phenylphosphorus[10] derivatives, and others form alkali-metal adducts. Fourth, the rupture of the C—Z bond in R—Z appears to be facilitated as the anionic stability of the fragments increases. For example, with $C_6H_5—Z$ the apparent ease of cleavage is $C_6H_5—F > C_6H_5—OCH_3 > C_6H_5—N(CH_3)_2$.[11] Also, with a given $Z(O—C_6H_5)$ enhanced stabilization of R^- promotes the C—Z bond rupture: $CH_2{=}CH—CH_2—O—C_6H_5$ cleaves much more readily than $CH_3—O—C_6H_5$.[12] Presumably the allyl anionic stability, anticipated in the transition state of bond cleavage, is a deciding factor.

[2] D. E. Paul, D. Lipkin, and S. I. Weissman, *J. Am. Chem. Soc.*, **78**, 116 (1956).

[3] R. L. Ward, *J. Chem. Phys.*, **32**, 1592 (1960).

[4] R. L. Ward, *J. Chem. Phys.*, **30**, 852 (1959).

[5] For $p\pi—p\pi$ effects in organoboranes, cf. T. D. Coyle, S. L. Stafford, and F. G. A. Stone, *J. Chem. Soc.*, **1961**, 3103; (b) for $d\pi—p\pi$ effects in organosilanes, cf. C. Eaborn, *Organosilicon Compounds*, Academic, New York, 1960, pp. 91–113.

[6] W. Grimme, K. Reinert, and R. Köster, *Tetrahedron Letters*, **1961** (18), 624.

[7] Cf. L. I. Zakharkin, *Bull. Acad. Sci. USSR* (*English Transl.*), **1964**, 182. Apparently any sodium metal adduction leads eventually to aluminum metal displacement and the formation of phenylsodium.

[8] (a) M. G. Townsend, *J. Chem. Soc.*, **1963**, 51; (b) R. D. Cowell, G. Urry, and S. I. Weissman, *J. Am. Chem. Soc.*, **85**, 222 (1963).

[9] J. J. Eisch and R. J. Beuhler, *J. Org. Chem.*, **28**, 2876 (1963).

[10] J. W. B. Reesor and G. F Wright, *J. Org. Chem.*, **22**, 285, 375, 382 (1957).

[11] J. J. Eisch, *J. Org. Chem.*, **28**, 707 (1963).

[12] J. J. Eisch and A. M. Jacobs, *J. Org. Chem.*, **28**, 2145 (1963).

2. Coupling:

a.
$$2[(C_6H_5)_2\overset{-}{C}\overset{H}{\underset{H}{-C}}\cdot]Na^+ \rightarrow (C_6H_5)_2\overset{-}{\underset{Na^+}{C}}-CH_2-CH_2-\overset{-}{\underset{Na^+}{C}}(C_6H_5)_2 \qquad (2-18)^{18b}$$

b.
$$2(C_6H_5)_3SiCH{=}CH_2 \xrightarrow{2Li} (C_6H_5)_3Si\overset{Li}{\underset{}{C}}HCH_2CH_2\overset{Li}{\underset{}{C}}HSi(C_6H_5)_3 \qquad (2-19)^9$$

c.

$$(2-20)^{17}$$

d.
$$2(C_6H_5)_2C{=}O \xrightarrow{2M} (C_6H_5)_2\overset{OM}{\underset{OM}{C}}-C(C_6H_5)_2 \qquad (2-21)^{18}$$

e.

$$(2-22)^{19a}$$

f.
$$2C_6H_5-CH{=}N-C_6H_5 \xrightarrow[THF]{2Na} $$

$$(90\% \ d, l)$$

$$(2-23)^{19b}$$

3. Electron transfer:

a. $2Na^+[(C_6H_5)_2C-C(C_6H_5)_2]^{--} +$

$$\longrightarrow (C_6H_5)_2C{=}C(C_6H_5)_2$$

$$+$$

$$(2-24)^{20}$$

[17] (a) B. Emmert, *Ber.*, **47**, 2598 (1914); **49**, 1060 (1916); **50**, 31 (1917); (b) J. J. Eisch and R. M. Thompson, *J. Org. Chem.*, **27**, 4171 (1962).
[18] (a) E. Beckmann and T. Paul, *Ann.*, **266**, 1 (1891); (b) W. Schlenk, J. Appenrodt, A. Michael, and A. Thal, *Ber.*, **47**, 473 (1914); (c) W. Schlenk and E. Bergmann, *Ann.*, **464**, 26 (1928).
[19] (a) L. I. Smith and H. H. Hoehn, *J. Am. Chem. Soc.*, **63**, 1184 (1941); (b) J. J. Eisch, D. D. Kaska, and C. J. Peterson, *J. Org. Chem.*, **31**, 453 (1966).
[20] E. Müller and G. Röscheisen, *Ber.*, **90**, 543 (1957).

b. $2Li^+ + (C_6H_5)_3N \longrightarrow C_6H_5-C_6H_5 + (C_6H_5)_2N-Li \quad (2\text{-}25)^{11}$
$+ C_6H_5Li$

c. $Na^+ +$ $\longrightarrow$ $+$ Na^+

$(2\text{-}26)^2$

As will be established subsequently, there exists much compelling physical evidence which has characterized the electronic nature of such 1:1 and 2:1 adducts. Therefore, since physical measurements and chemical behavior support the character of these stable metal adducts, it becomes relevant to ask whether analogous metal adducts occur as transitory intermediates in other metal-organic substrate interactions. If they do, they may determine the behavior and, hence, the products of such reaction systems. One reservation must be borne in mind, however: If a radical-anion intermediate is detected in a metal-organic substrate cleavage,

$$M + R-Z \longrightarrow M^+[R \div Z]^- \xrightarrow{M} M^+Z^- + R-M \qquad (2\text{-}27)$$

it may indicate the accumulation of a significant reaction intermediate. Ideally, though, the generation and disappearance of the key radical-anion intermediate should be related kinetically to the formation of metal reaction products. Nevertheless, the detection of specific radical anions in solution is a useful tool in such mechanistic studies. As in the formation of stable 1:1 metal-organic substrate adducts themselves, certain solvents, metals, and organic substrates would be expected to promote transitory metal adduct formation. The observation that more basic solvents, such as tetrahydrofuran, 1,2-dimethoxyethane, and tetrahydropyran, more active metals (lithium, sodium, and potassium), and polynuclear aromatic derivatives (naphthalene, biphenyl) facilitate the cleavage and coupling reactions of many organic systems with alkali metals suggests strongly that 1:1 or 2:1 metal-organic substrate adducts are key intermediates in these reactions.

To appreciate the role of such radical anion (1:1) or dianion (2:1) adducts in organic chemistry, a collection of apparently disparate observations can be considered. First, although fluorene will not react rapidly with lithium metal in ethyl ether, the same reaction proceeds spontaneously in tetrahydrofuran to yield fluorenyllithium. Although first reports assigned the fate of the displaced hydrogen to the formation of lithium hydride or molecular hydrogen,[21] [22] it has been shown that the hydrogen instead reduces part of the initial fluorene to hydrofluorenes.[16a] The transitory green color in the reaction mixture can be ascribed to the generation of radical anions or dianions, which act as strong bases toward the acidic hydrogens of fluorene. The analogy in behavior with the 1:1 lithium-biphenyl adduct should be apparent.

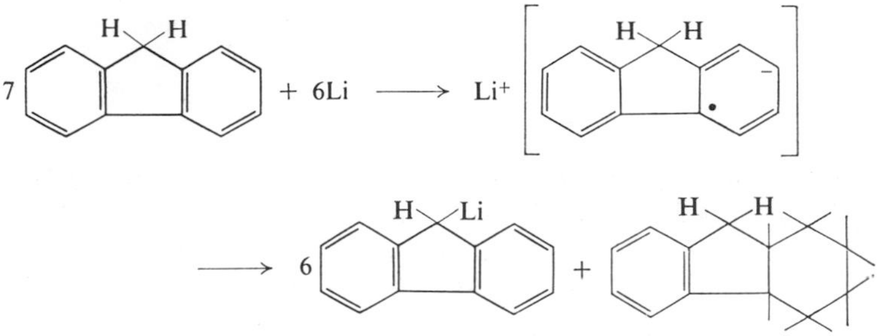

$$(2\text{-}28)^{16a}$$

A second example is the observation that although triphenylmethyl chloride is inert to sodium metal in ethyl ether, the addition of a small amount of bromobenzene initiates a prompt reaction. Moreover, the sodium halide formed consisted of 88 % sodium chloride. With excellent intuition the sodium "carrier" action of the bromobenzene was attributed to a metal halyl formation (A)[23]:

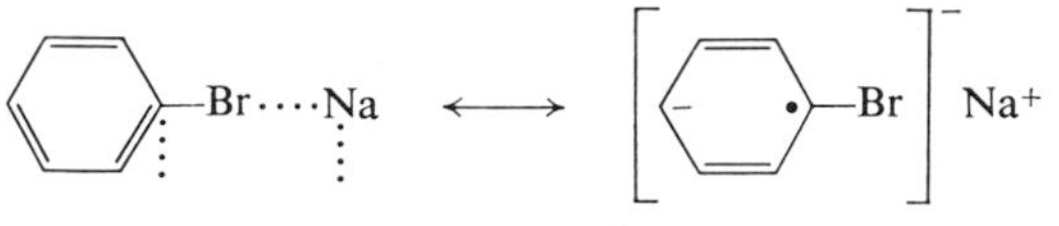

$$(2\text{-}29)$$

In more recent terms, this metal halyl would be described as a 1:1 sodium cation–radical anion pair (B).

Another instance of the apparent intermediacy of transitory metal adducts is the cleavage or coupling of biphenyl derivatives. Although the system reacts extremely slowly with lithium metal in ether, reaction in tetrahydrofuran solution occurs promptly, with the formation of green colors. The fact that biphenyl itself yields green-colored adducts readily under these conditions suggests the following mechanism:

[21] H. Gilman and R. Gorsich, *J. Org. Chem.*, **23**, 550 (1958).
[22] G. W. H. Scherf and R. K. Brown, *Can. J. Chem.*, **38**, 2450 (1960).
[23] A. A. Morton and J. R. Stevens, *J. Am. Chem. Soc.*, **54**, 1919 (1932).

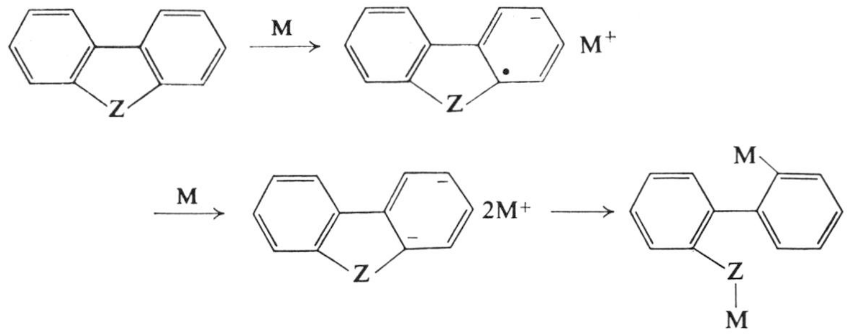

(2–30)

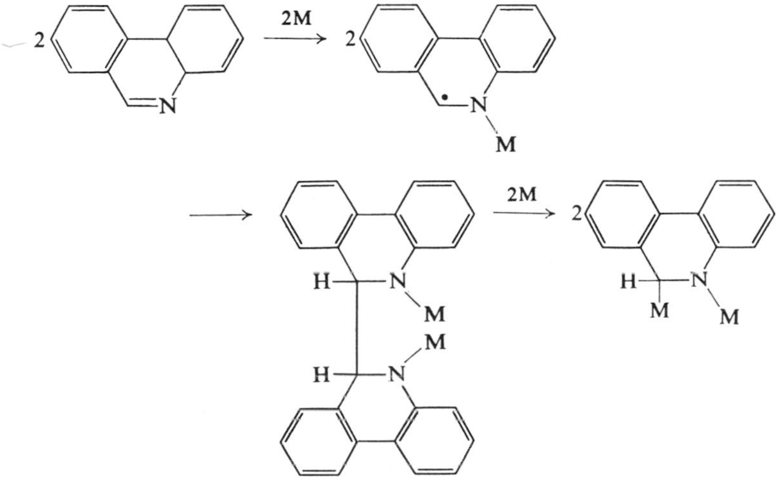

(2–31)

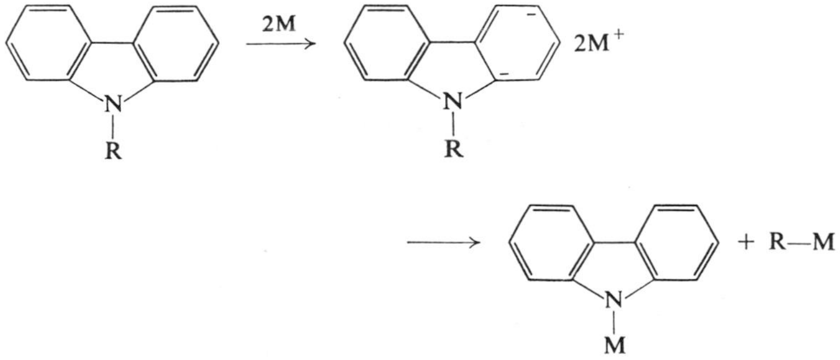

(2–32)

In a fourth case Müller and Töpel observed that the attempted preparation of 9-anthryllithium from 9-bromoanthracene and lithium metal caused much decomposition with the resultant formation of anthracene. This failure was ascribed to the high metalating power of 9-anthryllithium toward the ether. On the other hand, polynuclear aryllithium compounds prepared in other ways (that is, halogen-metal exchange) were shown to be stable in ether solution. The fact that the anthracene system forms metal adducts suggests that an intermediate metal halyl is the strong base responsible for attack on the ether[24]:

$$+ \text{M—Br} \qquad (2\text{–}33)$$

Other brief examples are the isomerization of *cis*-2-halostilbenes to *trans*-stilbene derivatives during the reaction with lithium metal[25]:

$$(2\text{–}34)$$

or the formation of perylene from 1,1'-binaphthyl and lithium in tetrahydro-furan[26]:

$$(2\text{–}35)$$

Finally, the classic German research on the polymerization of conjugated dienes by alkali metals can now be interpreted in terms of intermediate

[24] E. Müller and T. Töpel, *Ber.*, **72**, 273 (1939).
[25] D. F. Detar and Y. W. Chu, *J. Am. Chem. Soc.*, **77**, 4410 (1955).
[26] (a) J. J. Eisch, unpublished studies, 1961; (b) H. Gilman and C. G. Brannen, *J. Am. Chem. Soc.*, **71**, 657 (1949).

radical anions. Although with butadiene, for example, mechanisms involving either 2:1 or 1:1 metal-diolefin intermediates can be written, the present opinion favors a 1:1 adduct, which then can couple to form a dimeric dianion[27]:

$$2H_2C{=}CH{-}CH{=}CH_2 \xrightarrow{\ 2M\ } 2H_2\overset{\cdot}{C}{-}CH{=}CH{-}\overset{-}{C}H_2\overset{+}{M} \longrightarrow \begin{array}{c} \\ M^+ \\ H_2\overset{-}{C}{-}CH{=}CH{-}CH_2 \\ | \\ H_2\overset{-}{C}{-}CH{=}CH{-}CH_2 \\ M^+ \end{array} \qquad (2\text{--}36)$$

Polymerization then ensues by a multistep anionic attack on other butadiene molecules. Since such a process leads to the link-up of butadiene molecules in a 1,4-fashion, *cis-* or *trans-*disposition of groups about the central double bond can occur. In comparison with other alkali metals, lithium metal in non-polar solvents displays a remarkable specificity in polymerizing butadiene and isoprene, the principal product being the 1,4-*cis*-polyalkadiene.[28] The other alkali metals and, indeed, lithium metal itself in polar solvents form predominantly the 1,4-*trans*-polymer. Since this difference in chemical behavior seems intimately connected with the structural properties of metal alkyls, which will be treated in detail later, suffice it to say that the polar covalent character of carbon-lithium bonds leads to molecular association, especially in circumstances where the solvent cannot solvate the lithium atom center, $R{-}Li(OR_2)_n$, and hence diminish such association, $R{-}Li\cdots R{-}Li\cdots R{-}Li$. The more polar character of carbon bonds to sodium or higher alkali metals and the lessened Lewis acidity of such alkali-metal atom centers makes molecular associations less significant. Therefore, the stereospecificity of lithium metal polymerizations may stem from a coiling of the dilithio adduct dimer, so as to permit the Lewis acidity of the lithium atom to exploit the π-electrons of the double bonds within the dimer:

$$\longrightarrow \quad 1,4\text{-}cis\text{-polymer} \qquad (2\text{--}37)$$

[27] M. Szwarc, M. Levy, and R. Milkovich, *J. Am. Chem. Soc.*, **78**, 2656 (1956).
[28] Anon., *Ind. Eng. Chem.*, **48**, 778 (1956).

Further complexation of butadiene molecules in a cisoid fashion would be advantageous, as the Lewis acid character of the lithium would thus be more fruitfully utilized and the 1,4-addition could ensue most smoothly. The lithium center-unsaturated electron complexation would maintain the helical arrangement of the growing chain and hence yield the 1,4-*cis*-polymer. Consistent with this view is the adverse effect of added Lewis bases, such as amines and ethers. This coordination of the lithium cation by a Lewis base would detract from the complexing advantage of a coiled chain, and, as observed, promote the formation of the 1,2- and 1,4-*trans*-polymer.[29]

Physical Properties of Metal-Hydrocarbon Adducts[30,31,32]

Even though the addition of alkali metals to organic systems has been recognized for some 70 years, the nature of these adducts has been defined only by very recent physicochemical studies. In elucidating their structure key questions which have arisen concern the metal-organic substrate stoichiometry, the extent of electron transfer from the metal to the organic substrate, and the firmness of ion pairing between the potential metal cations and organic anions; in the latter case, molecular unit association could also be entertained. In the first place, the problem of stoichiometry has been attacked either by determining the solubility of a metal in a dilute solution of the organic substrate, or by the isolation and analysis of solid metal-organic substrate adducts. In this manner, 1:1 and 2:1 adducts have been detected with aromatic and aza-aromatic systems, aryl ketones, and aryl boranes. In certain instances, however, 2:1 adducts were assumed, even in the face of contrary experimental evidence. Thus, the 1:1 ratio observed between sodium and naphthalene in ether solvents was interpreted to mean that a complex was formed between a 2:1 adduct and 1 mole of naphthalene. This viewpoint, prompted by the chemical behavior of such adducts, has been disproved by recent spectroscopic measurements. There is some indication that lithium metal in more donor solvents can form higher than 2:1 adducts to some extent.

The extent of electron transfer from the metal atom to the organic substrate seems to depend upon whether solid adducts or solution species are under examination. From magnetic susceptibility and electrical conductance measurements on solid, solvent-free alkali metal–anthracene adducts (ca. 1:1 to 2:1), a model consisting of both neutral and ionized sodium atoms, and

[29] H. Morita and A. V. Tobolsky, *J. Am. Chem. Soc.*, **79**, 5853 (1957).
[30] W. A. Holmes-Walker and A. R. Ubbelohde, *J. Chem. Soc.*, **1954**, 720.
[31] G. J. Hoijtink et al., *Rec. trav. chim.*, **74**, 277 (1956); **75**, 487 (1956); **76**, 813, 834, 836, 860, 869 (1957).
[32] S. I. Weissman et al., *J. Phys. Chem.*, **61**, 28 (1957); *J. Am. Chem. Soc.*, **80**, 4549, 5342 (1958).

neutral and negative anthracene anions was postulated, wherein the electrons displayed a limited freedom of mobility in the crystal lattice. Although the marked electrostriction is in accord with electron transfer from the alkali metal to anthracene, the higher activation energy in the electrical conductivity indicates significant potential barriers to electron flow in the lattice and, hence, possibly a statistical, rather than a 100% stoichiometric, transfer of electrons. In dilute solution in donor solvents, however, several physical measurements point to complete electron transfer. The two most informative measurements are based upon the free radical character of 1:1 adducts. The paramagnetic susceptibilities of the 1:1 alkali-metal adducts of anthracene, biphenyl, naphthalene, phenanthrene and *m*-terphenyl, as measured by Gouy's method, fell in a range (1235–1260) to be expected for the presence of one unpaired electron per aromatic ring.[33] Moreover, the radical anions showed no tendency to dimerize. A more definitive measure of the intimacy of electron association with the aromatic system and a unique characterization of a given radical anion in solution is its electron spin resonance (e.s.r.) signal. The delocalized character of the unpaired electron spin in the π-cloud can be supported by the gyromagnetic ratio (*g*-value) of the signal, the breadth (in gauss) of the signal, and the number and intensity of the hyperfine splitting pattern.[34] As with nuclear magnetic resonance (n.m.r.) spectral signals, the e.s.r. signal can be split by the magnetic moments of the aromatic nuclear protons in a proportion to the unpaired spin density at the C—H center in question. Such e.s.r. data often allow the nature of the organic system bearing the free radical to be identified unambiguously. However, it should be remembered that the complexity of a particular e.s.r. hyperfine pattern can be obscured by rapid electron exchange between the original organic substrate and the radical anion. Thus, although the naphthalene radical anion was reported at first to yield a 17-line hyperfine splitting pattern, it later revealed a 25-line pattern.

Many metal adducts of both 2:1 and 1:1 stoichiometry show no paramagnetic behavior, and hence display no paramagnetic susceptibility nor e.s.r. signal. For 2:1 adducts, as of the disodio adduct of anthracene in solution, it is assumed that both electrons occupy the same nondegenerate antibonding molecular orbital and hence their spins are paired in the dianion. Certain metal 1:1 adducts, such as the sodium adducts of triphenylborane and the boroindanes, are dimagnetic,[35] apparently because of dimerization to species such as

[33] T. L. Chu and S. C. Yu, *J. Am. Chem. Soc.*, **76**, 3367 (1954).

[34] D. J. E. Ingram, *Free Radicals as Studied by Electron Spin Resonance*, Butterworth, London, 1958.

[35] (a) T. L. Chu, *J. Am. Chem. Soc.*, **75**, 1730 (1953); (b) W. Grimme, K. Reinert, and R. Köster, *Tetrahedron Letters*, **1961** (8), 624.

$$2M^+[(C_6H_5)_3B\!-\!B(C_6H_5)_3]^{--} \quad \text{or} \quad 2M^+ \qquad\qquad\qquad\qquad (2\text{–}38)$$

In regard to the firmness of the metal cation-aromatic anion pairing in ether solvents, the conductance of such solutions does support the presence of ionic species, but the low value (at 7.1×10^{-4} m/l = 9.6; of acetic acid in water, 1×10^{-3} m/l = 48.6) suggests intimate ion pairing, even in highly dilute solution.

A further consideration of metal adducts concerns their most striking property: their intense and esthetically pleasing colors (blue, green, red, orange) in solution. Resulting from colorless organic substrates, such colors signify longer-wavelength and hence lower-energy electronic transitions in the adducts. The retention of almost the same ultraviolet bands as the original hydrocarbon suggests that the metal adduction occurs with no drastic disturbance in the parent compound's energy levels, but simply by occupancy of higher levels by the accepted electron. Such characteristic optical absorption spectra have been utilized in studying electron transfer between dissimilar organic substrates. Admixing a hydrocarbon A with the preformed metal adduct of hydrocarbon B allows an equilibrium test of relative electron affinities:

$$A + M^+[\overset{\bullet}{B}]^- \;\rightleftharpoons\; B + M^+[\overset{\bullet}{A}]^- \qquad\qquad (2\text{–}39)$$

In this manner the increasing order of electron affinities has been established: benzene < phenanthrene < naphthalene < anthracene < naphthacene. A more quantitative order of reduction potentials was achieved by electrolytic reduction.[36]

In conclusion, additional research must be done to ascertain the geometrical relationship of the metal and organic centers in these adducts. Most desirable would be X-ray crystallographic examination of crystalline metal-hydrocarbon solvates, as, for example, the 2:1 adduct of lithium and biphenyl in tetrahydrofuran. Whether the formal similarity of these alkali metal adducts to bis(arene) transition metal complexes [for example, $(C_6H_6)_2Cr$] has any basis in fact will have to await such a structural analysis.

---

[36] (a) A. T. Watson and F. A. Matsen, *J. Chem. Phys.*, **18**, 1305 (1950); (b) I. Bergman, *Trans. Faraday Soc.*, **50**, 829 (1954).

Replacement Reactions

Suitable organic substrates for metal replacement reactions can be either saturated or unsaturated. It has already been mentioned that alkyl halides, alkyl ethers, and metal alkyls are suitable substrates for the preparation of organometallic compounds. However, unsaturated organic compounds show a greater diversity of reactions with active metals, especially those of the alkali and alkaline earth families. Indeed, certain labile carbon-carbon bonds, as in *sym*-tetraphenylethane, *unsym*-tetraphenylethane, and pentaphenylethane, can be cleaved with metallic potassium or with lithium metal (as the 2:1 lithium-biphenyl adduct[11]):

$$(C_6H_5)_2CH—CH(C_6H_5)_2 + 2Li \rightarrow 2(C_6H_5)_2CHLi \quad (85\%) \qquad (2\text{-}40)$$

Pseudoacidic hydrocarbons, such as cyclopentadiene, 1-alkynes, and triaryl-alkanes, can liberate hydrogen with alkali metals, especially in ether and liquid ammonia solution[37]:

$$(2\text{-}41)$$

The metal cleavage of mercury aryls exemplifies the metal rupture of a carbon bonded to an electropositive element, and hence this reaction resembles the replacement of hydrogen just mentioned. The preparation of phenyllithium is typical[38]:

$$(C_6H_5)_2Hg + 2Li \rightarrow 2C_6H_5Li + Hg \qquad (2\text{-}42)$$

Since this reaction can be conducted in nondonor solvents such as benzene, the phenyllithium thereby obtained is free of ether or lithium halide complexation. Hence, for certain physical and chemical studies, this method of preparation is superior to that employing bromobenzene and lithium metal in ether solution. In this context it is appropriate to mention that bonds between Group IVA atoms can be made and be ruptured by alkali metals. The preparation of triphenylsilyllithium in a discrete two-step process from chlorotriphenylsilane illustrates this point[39]:

$$2(C_6H_5)_3SiCl \xrightarrow{2Li} (C_6H_5)_3Si—Si(C_6H_5)_3 \xrightarrow{2Li} 2(C_6H_5)_3SiLi \qquad (2\text{-}43)$$
$$+ \quad 2LiCl$$

[37] C. B. Wooster and N. W. Mitchell, *J. Am. Chem. Soc.*, **52**, 688 (1930).

[38] G. Wittig, F. J. Meyer, and G. Lange, *Ann.*, **571**, 167 (1951).

[39] (a) H. Gilman and G. D. Lichtenwalter, *J. Am. Chem. Soc.*, **80**, 608 (1958); (b) D. Wittenberg and H. Gilman, *Quart. Rev. (London)*, **13**, 116 (1959).

However, attempts to extrapolate this reaction to aluminum aryls have thus far yielded only metal-metal exchange and cleavage products[40]:

$$2(C_6H_5)AlCl \xrightarrow{3Na} 2C_6H_5Na + Al + NaCl \tag{2-44}$$

Finally, aryl halides (even fluorobenzene), sulfides, amines, and vinyl ethers, cleave most readily when an alkali metal in tetrahydrofuran solution is taken[41]:

$$C_6H_5F + 2Li \longrightarrow C_6H_5Li + LiF \tag{2-45}$$

$$C_6H_5-OCH_2CH=CH_2 + 2Li \longrightarrow C_6H_5OLi + CH_2=CHCH_2Li \tag{2-46}$$

$$(C_6H_5)_3N + 2Li \longrightarrow C_6H_5Li + (C_6H_5)_2N-Li \tag{2-48}$$

Predisposing Experimental Conditions

In planning the synthesis of an organometallic compound from the free metal, or in deciding to employ a metal in an organic reaction, the foregoing principles and correlations can be most helpful. To further illustrate their application, this section considers experimental situations where conditions can be chosen to enhance the chances of a successful reaction.

In the first place, the nature of the metal alkyl desired will put severe limitations upon preparations starting from the metal. The most suitable metals, of course, are the alkali and alkaline earth metals, all of which react with organic halides or ethers (R—Z) to form organometallics:

$$2M + R-Z \rightarrow R-M + MZ \tag{2-49}$$

Here the major problem consists in choosing a suitable solvent and condition under which to mix and preserve the resulting RM type. Scrupulously anhydrous media and an inert atmosphere of nitrogen, helium, or argon must be maintained at all times. The solvent may be an ether or an alkane hydrocarbon, although the former cannot be used for the more reactive alkali metal

[40] J. J. Eisch and W. C. Kaska, unpublished studies, 1961.
[41] H. Gilman and J. J. Dietrich, *J. Org. Chem.*, **22**, 851 (1957).

alkyls, due to their instability in this medium. To moderate the vigor of the reaction and to minimize side reactions, the metal should be highly pure and have an uncorroded surface. Depending upon individual metal reactivity, it may be advantageous to deal with highly subdivided metal powder or dispersions (high specific surface area) or to use a large excess of metal to guarantee prompt reaction. With less active metals it may be necessary to work at elevated temperatures in the absence of solvent and to employ various promoters (cf. *infra*).[42] Illustrative is the formation of ethylaluminum sesquichloride from aluminum chips and ethyl chloride[43]:

$$3CH_3CH_2Cl + 2Al \rightarrow (CH_3CH_2)_2AlCl + CH_3CH_2AlCl_2 \qquad (2\text{--}50)$$

or the reaction of antimony with trifluoromethyl iodide[44]:

$$F_3CI + Sb \rightarrow (CF_3)_3Sb + (CF_3)_2SbI + CF_3SbI_2 \qquad (2\text{--}51)$$

Thus, metals and metalloids of Groups IA, IIA, IIB, IIIA, IVA, VA, and VIA have been reported to react with organic halides in the foregoing manner,[45] with the exception of boron and gallium. The former possibly owes its inertness to a very compact crystal structure (hardness, 9.2; m.p. 2300°), while the latter easily forms an oxide covering and, being a liquid above 30°, has a low specific surface. (However, gallium metal can be made to react readily with allyl or benzyl halides, although it is inert to ethyl halides under ordinary conditions.)[46] In certain cases, alloys with more active metals, such as sodium, or with transition metals, such as copper, are used to promote reaction:

$$2Hg(Na) + 2R\text{---}X \rightarrow R_2Hg + NaX \qquad (2\text{--}52)$$

$$Si(Cu) + CH_3Cl \rightarrow (CH_3)_nSiCl_{4-n} \qquad (2\text{--}53)$$

Thus, the experimental consequences of lessened metal reactivity due to higher metal sublimation energies and ionization potentials can be seen as one goes from alkali metals to metalloids.

Second, as to the nature of the organic halide or ether (R—Z) employed in the metal reaction, the principal noteworthy distinction is that when R is allylic or benzylic and Z is iodide, the reactivity of RZ, in general, appears

---

[42] For example, in the preparation of the Blaise reagent (RZnX) from zinc metal and organic halides, the use of a zinc-copper couple is advantageous: A. Job and R. Reich, *Bull. soc. chim. France*, **33** (4), 414 (1924).

[43] (a) A. V. Grosse and J. M. Mavity, *J. Org. Chem.*, **5**, 106 (1940); (b) K. Ziegler and H. Martin, *Makromol. Chem.*, **18–19**, 186 (1956).

[44] J. W. Dale, H. J. Emeleus, R. N. Haszeldine, and J. H. Moss, *J. Chem. Soc.*, **1957**, 3708.

[45] R. G. Jones and H. Gilman, *Chem. Rev.*, **54**, 835 (1954).

[46] J. J. Eisch, unpublished studies, 1956.

to be at a maximum. Inherent in these observations are both the smaller bond dissociation energies of the C—I linkage versus other C—X bonds and the relative stability of any allylic radical or anionic character of the leaving R group in the transition state of cleavage of R—X (cf. Eq. 2–3). At present, there is little definitive information about the effect of the primary, secondary, or tertiary nature of R and the reactivity of R—Z, but primary halides do appear to be more responsive to metals.[47]

Third, the type of solvent employed in such metal-organic substrate interactions can influence the chances of a successful reaction very dramatically. As would follow from the Born-Haber treatment of these reactions, metal cation solvation can contribute substantially to a favorable energy change. Kinetic consequences of this thermodynamic promotion are that the better the solvating character of the solvent, the more rapidly does the metal interact with the organic substrate. Since hydrocarbons are the least basic in this sense, metal reactions conducted in such systems usually demand scrupulous removal of impurities and other retarding conditions and the maintenance of an active metal surface. Recent introduction of more basic ether,[48] amine,[49a,b] and sulfide[49c] solvents has facilitated the preparation of many organometallic compounds. Some of the most useful new solvents are dimethyl ether, tetrahydrofuran, 1,2-dimethoxyethane, diethyleneglycol dimethyl ether, N,N-dimethylformamide, and N-methylpyrrolidine.

Fourth, several methods of promoting metal reactions have been developed. These can be classified into various types. There are the metal oxide surface cleaners, such as the use of halogen (iodine or bromine) or reactive alkyl halides (methyl iodide, ethylene bromide, or ethyl bromide, as in entrainment procedures[50]). Also, the inclusion of the corresponding metal halide (for example, anhydrous magnesium bromide in Grignard preparations) seems to be advantageous as a moisture-scavenging agent. In addition, with alkali metals the use of aromatic hydrocarbons, such as biphenyl and naphthalene, which form 1:1 or 2:1 alkali metal adducts, permits more facile reaction via the solubilized form of metal presented to the organic substrate.[11,51] Finally, the metal may be employed as an alloy with mercury, copper, or a more reactive alkali metal like sodium, in order to facilitate reaction. Involved in the behavior of such alloy systems is undoubtedly a

[47] M. S. Kharasch and O. Reinmuth, *Grignard Reactions of Nonmetallic Substances*, Prentice-Hall, Englewood Cliffs, N.J., 1954.

[48] (a) H. Normant, *Bull. soc. chim. France*, **1957**, 728; (b) H. E. Ramsden, A. E. Balint, W. R. Whitford, J. J. Walburn, and R. Cserr, *J. Org. Chem.*, **22**, 1202 (1957).

[49] Cf. (a) H. Normant, T. Cuvigny, J. Normant, and B. Angelo, *Bull. soc. chim. France*, **1965**, 1561; (b) G. Fraenkel, S. H. Ellis, and D. T. Dix, *J. Am. Chem. Soc.*, **87**, 1406 (1965), for the use of hexamethylphosphorotriamide; (c) G. Bähr and K. H. Thiele, *Ber.*, **70**, 1578 (1957), have prepared Grignard reagents in dimethyl sulfide.

[50] D. E. Pearson, D. Cowan, and J. D. Becker, *J. Org. Chem.*, **24**, 504 (1959).

[51] N. D. Scott, J. F. Walker, and V. L. Hansley, *J. Am. Chem. Soc.*, **58**, 2442 (1936).

combination of effects, such as maintenance of fresh metal surface, metal-metal alkyl exchange, and galvanic metal couples.

Fifth, the experimental execution of metal-organic substrate reactions can be crucial to a successful procedure. Since the systems employed are heterogeneous, efficient mixing is very important. To this end, attention should be directed to the use of fine metal dispersions, high-speed stirring of metal dispersions by ultrasonics,[52] creased reaction flasks, and refluxing solvent systems above the melting point of the alkali metal.[53] Although photochemical and thermal promotion of metal reactions is often useful, excessively high temperatures and prolonged illumination usually cause undesirable side reactions.

Although the foregoing discussion was directed principally at the cleavage reactions of metals with organic halides (R—Z) and with ethers (R—O—R'), the remarks are equally valid for a third type of reaction, the metal-metal exchange or displacement reaction:

$$M + R\text{—}M' \rightarrow M' + R\text{—}M \qquad (2\text{--}54)$$

However, thermodynamic factors, rather than kinetic factors, often limit the feasibility of this reaction. This latter reaction differs from the previous ones, in that this system can involve a ready equilibrium between R—M' and R—M. Since the interaction is the formal oxidation of M and the deposition of M', a high oxidation potential for M and as low a potential for M' as possible would seem most advantageous. In practice, the air-stable, readily accessible mercury alkyls are employed for R—M'. Usually the active metal M (alkali metals) is employed in excess; hence, its amalgamation with the liberated mercury furnishes additional driving force for the reaction. However, when M is a less active metal, an equilibrium mixture of both alkyls (R—M and R—M') is formed.[54] This seems to be the case with thallium and, possibly, gallium.[55]

[52] W. Slough and A. R. Ubbelohde, *J. Chem. Soc.*, **1957**, 918.
[53] Cf., *inter alia, Using Sodium in Dispersed Form*, pamphlet, Ethyl Corporation, New York.
[54] G. E. Coates and R. A. Whitcombe, *J. Chem. Soc.*, **1956**, 3351.
[55] J. J. Eisch, unpublished observation, 1956.

THREE
Structure of Organometallic Compounds

In the introductory chapter, structural features were considered briefly that account for the multiplicity of the known and of the possible organometallic compounds. Because of auto-association, complexation, and solvation phenomena, it is essential to consider first the gross structure of organometallic species, before a detailed electronic discussion of the carbon-metal bond is undertaken in the next chapter. Points of concern in such a discussion of structure are aspects such as the precise molecular or ionic aggregate present in different solvents or physical states, the three-dimensional arrangements of the submolecular units in these aggregates, the possible solution equilibria between distinct aggregates, and finally the over-all polarity of the individual organometallic species. Without the foregoing information, a discussion of the physical and chemical properties of organometallic compounds in terms of the polarity of an idealized, isolated carbon-metal bond is unjustifiable and meaningless. With the fruits of molecular structure research firmly in mind, one cannot only hope to find correlations between structure and physical properties, but can also hope to interpret qualitative and quantitative differences in organometallic chemical behavior in realistic electronic terms.

Despite the desirability of completely defining the nature of the different organometallic compounds, such unambiguous structural information is obtained only by arduous and ingenious research. The following discussion will give abundant witness to the incompleteness of our structural knowledge for many systems and to the pitfalls of experimentation and interpretation in obtaining the necessary data. But this discussion also presents the prospect of the real progress being made in this challenging research area.

Degree of Association

The metal alkyls of Groups IA, IIA, and IIIA give apparent molecular weights which are often integral multiples of the simple formula weights. The degree of association, which is the ratio of observed molecular weight to the formula weight, can vary from 2 (dimer) to quite a large number (polymer), depending upon the nature of the metal center, the size and electronic character of the alkyl group, and the medium in which the metal alkyl is dispersed. Illustrative of these aggregates are the classical instances of dimeric structures, as with trimethylaluminum, $[(CH_3)_3Al]_2$,[1] and, bearing in mind the metal alkyl–metal hydride parallel, diborane, $[BH_3]_2$.[2] At the other extreme are the ionic crystal lattice, as in the case of presumably ionic methylsodium, $[(Na^+)(CH_3^-)]_n$,[3] the molecular crystal of aluminum carbide, $(Al_4C_3)_n$,[4] and the linear repeating linkage in dimethylberyllium, $[(CH_3)_2Be]_n$,[5] all of which are different polymeric variants of the simple formulas.[6]

The foregoing degrees of association hold true only for the pure solid or liquid compounds, or for their solutions in solvents of low polarity. The presence of solvent molecules possessing Lewis basic character (B:) tends to favor depolymerization of the metal alkyl. Thus, metal alkyl autocomplexation can be impeded by solution in ethers or amines and even by admixture with metallic halides or ionic metal alkyls. (B: $= R_2O$, $R_3N:$, $:\ddot{X}:^-$, or $R:^-$). The variety of association phenomena among alkyls and alkyl metal hydrides can be appreciated from scanning the entries listed in Table 3-1.

Insight into the bonding responsible for such associations has been attained only after many false starts. It is true that many carbon-metal bonds are highly polar ($\overset{\delta-}{C}{-}\overset{\delta+}{M}$) and that mutual alignment of such polar linkages in individual metal alkyl units might be pictured as the driving force for such association. Dipolar interactions would be expected to be very indiscriminate

[1] P. H. Lewis and R. E. Rundle, *J. Chem. Phys.*, **16**, 552 (1948).
[2] (a) D. T. Hurd, *Introduction to the Chemistry of the Hydrides*, Wiley, New York, 1952; (b) F. G. A. Stone, in *Advances in Inorganic Chemistry and Radiochemistry*, Vol. II (H. J. Emeleus and A. G. Sharpe, eds.), Academic, New York, 1960, pp. 279–313.
[3] W. H. Carothers and D. D. Coffman, *J. Am. Chem. Soc.*, **52**, 1254 (1930).
[4] M. von Stackelberg and E. Schnorrenberg, *Z. Physik. Chem.* (*Leipzig*), **B27**, 37 (1934).
[5] A. I. Snow and R. E. Rundle, *Acta Cryst.*, **4**, 348 (1951).
[6] Conventional polymerization of certain unsaturated organoaluminum compounds also has resulted in polymeric metal alkyls, but not of the electron-deficient bonding type considered here. Cf. D. Braun, *Angew. Chem.*, **73**, 197 (1961).

TABLE 3–1

Association of Metal Alkyls

Compound	Medium	Degree of Association	Ref.
CH_3Li	Ethyl ether	3	a
C_2H_5Li	Benzene	6	b
C_6H_5Li	Ethyl ether	2	a
C_2H_5MgCl	Ethyl ether	2	c
C_2H_5MgCl	Tetrahydrofuran	1	c
$(CH_3CH)_2Be$ | CH_3	Benzene	2	d
$(C_2H_5)_3Al$	Benzene	2	e
$(CH_3CHCH_2)_3Al$ | CH_3	Benzene	1	f
$(C_2H_5)_2AlH$	Benzene	3	f
$(C_2H_5)_3Ga$	Benzene	1–2	g, i
$(CH_3)_3In$	Benzene	4 (1)	h, i

[a] G. Wittig, F. J. Meyer, and G. Lange, *Ann.*, **571**, 167 (1951).
[b] T. L. Brown and M. T. Rogers, *J. Am. Chem. Soc.*, **79**, 1859 (1957).
[c] E. C. Ashby and W. E. Becker, *J. Am. Chem. Soc.*, **85**, 118 (1963).
[d] G. E. Coates and F. Glockling, *J. Chem. Soc.*, 22 (1953).
[e] K. S. Pitzer and H. S. Gutowsky, *J. Am. Chem. Soc.*, **68**, 2204 (1946).
[f] E. G. Hoffmann, *Ann.*, **629**, 104 (1960).
[g] L. M. Dennis and W. Patnode, *J. Am. Chem. Soc.*, **54**, 182 (1932).
[h] E. L. Amma and R. E. Rundle, *J. Am. Chem. Soc.*, **80**, 4141 (1958): for the crystalline state.
[i] N. Muller and A. L. Otermat, *Inorg. Chem.*, **4**, 296 (1965).

as to the number of metal alkyl units clustered together. However, as more reliable structural information emerges from the X-ray crystallographic examination of such systems, one is struck by the selectivity which metal alkyls exhibit both in the degree of polymerization and the geometric array of units. In addition, the fact that bond polarity bears no compelling relationship to association tendency is demonstrated by the tetrameric nature of tetramethylplatinum ($[CH_3]_4Pt]_4$, where $X_{Pt} = 1.44$), compared with the monomeric character of dimethylmercury ($X_{Hg} = 1.44$ on the Allred-Rochow scale).[7] Since most associated metal alkyls have metal centers in the monomer

[7] R. E. Rundle, *J. Phys. Chem.*, **61**, 45 (1957).

which lack an electronic octet and since electron-pair donors to such Lewis acid metal centers interfere with metal alkyl association, it appears that merely the polarity of the carbon-metal bond is insufficient for association and that an unoccupied, low-lying *p*-orbital or *d*-orbital is required for auto-complexation. If one then views such an association as a Lewis acid–Lewis base interaction involving the available *p*-orbital on the metal, the question as to the source of the bonding electron pair arises. To meet this difficulty and to suggest that this association is only a special case of a more general structural phenomenon, Rundle has proposed a theory of electron-deficient bonding, applicable in situations where the number of available bonding electrons is insufficient to fill the low-lying molecular orbitals involved.[7] At one extrapolated extreme would be the structure of metals themselves, where a very insufficient number of electrons is employed in bonding together the metal nuclei (multicenter molecular orbitals) in a most cohesive fashion while at the same time enjoying a great mobility among the array of atoms (high thermal and electrical conductivity, ductility, and malleability). At the other end of the gamut of electron-deficient bonding would be three-center orbitals formed between two hybridized *p*-orbitals of the metal centers and the *sp*-hybridized orbital of the alkyl group (I):

I

Being shared between the two metal atoms, the alkyl group is said to be "bridged." Experimental support for the equal sharing of the alkyl group in metal alkyls rests upon the equidistant separation of the methyl group from the aluminum centers in trimethylaluminum dimer,[1,8] as determined by X-ray measurements, and upon the appearance of two nonequivalent methyl signals in the low-temperature n.m.r. spectrum of the same compound, pointing to two distinct magnetic environments for these methyl groups.[9]

The role of the metal center in associated metal alkyls can then be seen as one of furnishing an available *p*- or *d*-orbital for such multicenter bonding.

[8] E. L. Amma, private communication, 1964.
[9] N. Muller and D. E. Pritchard, *J. Am. Chem. Soc.*, **82**, 248 (1960).

In the first short period it is noteworthy that the oligomeric character of lithium alkyls, $(RLi)_n$ (where $n = 4$–6),[10] and the linear polymeric character of beryllium alkyls, $(R_2Be)_n$, can be developed from a straightforward molecular orbital extrapolation of Rundle's theory. However, despite the dimeric character of BH_3, boron alkyls themselves are monomeric.[11] Presumably the rather acute angle of the B—C—B group necessary to achieve overlap

II

of the boron orbitals with the hybrid methyl orbital would bring the boron centers too close to each other. Hence, metal-metal center repulsions would occur. Another factor which may be important would be the energy cost in rehybridizing the boron from sp^2 to sp^3; the short C—B bonds may make methyl-methyl repulsions severe in the tetrahedral configuration (II). In the second short period the increasing metal atom size removes the steric handicap to association with the aluminum alkyls (dimeric) and decreases the concentration of nuclear charge (and hence their polarizing power) with sodium and magnesium alkyls. As a consequence, the latter metal alkyls tend to display ionic association in their crystal lattices. This trend toward ionic character and ionic crystallinity appears to increase with the metal alkyls of higher members of Groups IA and IIA. On the other hand, dimerization of Group IIIA metal alkyls is hindered by the increasing metal-metal center repulsions of the larger nuclei in the prospective dimer structure. Trimethylthallium, for example, is monomeric in benzene solution.[12] As to the ability of σ-bonded transition metal alkyls to associate, the limited stability of the unsolvated R_nM type has precluded the formulation of the broad trends. A noteworthy exception, however, is the clearly tetrameric character of tetramethylplatinum, which was the first electron-deficient compound whose structure was surely established.[13]

From a perusal of the "bridging" character of such associated metal alkyls, the effect of changing the nature of the alkyl group can be appreciated. Thus, as one progresses along the series, $(CH_3)_3Al$, $(CH_3CH_2)_3Al$, $(i\text{-}C_3H_7)_3Al$, and $(i\text{-}C_4H_9)_3Al$, the association tendency of R_3Al wanes from a firm dimerization ($R = CH_3$) to a completely monomeric alkyl ($R = i\text{-}C_4H_9$). The nonbonded atom repulsions (steric hindrance) would be expected to disfavor

[10] T. L. Brown, D. W. Dickerhoof, and D. A. Bafus, *J. Am. Chem. Soc.*, **84**, 1371 (1962).
[11] W. Gerrard, *Organic Chemistry of Boron*, Academic, New York, 1961, p. 118.
[12] H. Gilman and R. G. Jones, *J. Am. Chem. Soc.*, **68**, 517 (1946).
[13] R. E. Rundle and J. H. Sturdivant, *J. Am. Chem. Soc.*, **69**, 1561 (1947).

association as R increases in size. Again, with a small "degenerate" alkyl (R = H), association is most favored. Thus, even diisobutylaluminum hydride is firmly trimeric in benzene solution, presumably with hydride bridges.[14] Although such size considerations give an adequate picture of bridging tendencies for saturated groups, the situation changes markedly with unsaturated groups. This is especially apparent with the vinylic and acetylenic derivatives of Group IIIA. Trivinylaluminum,[15] trivinylgallium,[16] and 1-butenyldiethylaluminum[17] all appear to be more firmly associated than their saturated counterparts. Since it appears altogether possible that the π-cloud adjacent to the metal atom is important in enhancing bridge bonding, strictly speaking these derivatives may not be electron-deficient compounds. Simple coordinate donation, as is operative in the association of Group IIIA chlorides and alkoxides, may be involved (III):

$$
\begin{array}{c}
\underset{R}{\overset{R}{\diagdown}}M\underset{:Z}{\overset{Z:}{\diagup}}M\underset{R}{\overset{R}{\diagup}} \qquad Z = R'-\ddot{O}: ; \ -Cl; \ -\overset{H}{\underset{|}{C}}=\overset{H}{\underset{|}{C}}-R'; \ -C\equiv C-R.
\end{array}
$$

III

A more confident molecular orbital description of the bridging will have to await reliable information on interatomic distances from X-ray crystallographic studies. Little is known at present about the association of metal alkyls containing unsaturation further removed from the carbon-metal bond than at the α,β-position.

Besides the metal center and the alkyl group, the solvent is important in determining the degree of association. Thus, the associated Group III alkyls form stable monomeric etherates in ether solution and amines in tertiary amine media. And, significantly, usually the degree of association of Grignard reagents and organolithium compounds[18] is higher in nonpolar solvents, such as hexane or benzene, than in ether. Further, the etherate of optically active *tris*(1)2-methylbutylaluminum is stable to racemization up to 100°C (IV), but in the absence of ether and in the presence of triisobutylaluminum the

$$(CH_3CH_2\underset{\underset{CH_3}{|}}{C}HCH_2)_3Al \leftarrow :\ddot{O}(CH_2CH_3)_2$$

IV

$$R-\underset{\underset{B}{\diagdown}}{M}\overset{\overset{R}{|}}{-}(CH_2)_n$$

V

[14] E. G. Hoffmann, *Ann.*, **629**, 104 (1960).
[15] B. Bartocha, A. J. Bilbo, D. E. Bublitz, and M. Y. Gray, *Z. Naturforsch.*, **16b**, 357 (1961).
[16] J. P. Oliver and L. G. Stevens, *J. Inorg. Nucl. Chem.*, **24**, 953 (1962).
[17] G. Wilke and H. Müller, *Ann.*, **629**, 222 (1960).
[18] T. L. Brown, D. W. Dickerhoof, and D. A. Bafus, *J. Am. Chem. Soc.*, **84**, 1371 (1962).

compound loses its optical activity very readily.[19] Finally, monomeric unsymmetrical aluminum alkyls have been prepared which are remarkably stable to disproportionation, and similarly stable boron derivatives have been devised (V), by providing the system with an internal Lewis base center for intramolecular complexation.[20] All these observations support the view that either intramolecular or intermolecular complexation by virtue of the available metal center orbitals and electron donor centers decreases the auto-complexation opportunity of the metal alkyl itself.

Over and above this type of association, one often encounters oligomers of metal alkyls which do not involve any apparent "violation" of the ordinary rules of valence. Indeed, such oligomers are favored, in order to avoid the existence of exceptional valence states and strained ring systems. Since the real oligomeric structure is an integral multiple of some empirical formula, careful molecular weight estimates are essential to a proper structure assignment. Compounds such as arsenobenzene (C_6H_5—As=As—C_6H_5) (VI),[21] *o*-phenylenemercury (Hg-*o*-C_6H_4) (VII),[22] and the diiododiphenylgermirene system

$$C_6H_5C=C-C_6H_5$$

(VIII),[23] lose much of their bizarre flavor when one learns that they are actually oligomers of these parent structures:

| VI | VII | VIII |

[19] P. Pino, L. Lardicci, and G. P. Lorenzi, *Angew. Chem.*, **70**, 599 (1958).
[20] (a) G. Bähr and G. E. Müller, *Ber.*, **88**, 251 (1955); (b) R. L. Letsinger and I. Skoog, *J. Am. Chem. Soc.*, **77**, 2491 (1955).
[21] S. E. Rasmussen and J. Danielsen, *Acta Chim. Scand.*, **14**, 1862 (1960).
[22] D. Grdenic, *Ber.*, **92**, 231 (1959).
[23] N. E. Volpin and D. N. Kursanov, *Zh. Obshch. Khim.*, **32**, 1455 (1962).

From the sad experience of researchers in this field, it should be noted that many of the accepted methods of molecular-weight determination are not without their individual Achilles' heel.

Complexation and Attendant Equilibria

Although really only a special case of auto-complexation, the solution behavior of certain types of organometallic compounds is at once so complicated and of such general interest that it deserves particular attention. In the case of systems, R_nMZ_{m-n}, formally containing at least two different groups bonded to a metal of valence m, one can speak of mixed metal alkyls (when Z = halide, alkoxide, or other acid radical) or unsymmetrical simple alkyls (when Z = alkyl group different from R). Such systems show a pronounced tendency to equilibrate with the fully symmetrical and, in the case of metals having a valence of $m > 2$, all the other possible combinations of ligands:

$$R_nMZ_{m-n} \rightleftharpoons R_mM + R_{m-1}MZ + \cdots + RMZ_{m-1} \qquad (3\text{-}1)$$

For the very engaging situation of divalent metals, the much-studied formation of the symmetrical products has been termed symmetrization or disproportionation:

$$2 \ RMZ \rightleftharpoons R_2M + MZ_2 \qquad (3\text{-}2)$$

Since an equilibrium is set up, the same point can be reached by mixing R_2M and MZ_2. In this case the reaction is often referred to as a redistribution of groups. Depending upon the particular organometallic system one is dealing with, however, such interchanges can be slow and the equilibrium point may be attained only after considerable heating in the presence of Lewis acid or peroxide catalysts.

Before enlarging upon the scope of this important exchange equilibrium, further complications must be noted. First, the admixture of R_2M and MZ_2 can lead to a metastable complex, $R_2M \cdot MZ_2$, in which redistribution of groups has not yet occurred. Second, as seen in the previous section, with certain metal alkyls in electron-pair donor solvents, a number of solvent molecules are intimately associated with the species discussed above. Third, in solvents of low polarity certain organometallics will be oligomeric to a variable degree. Thus, a generalized prospect of such complex equilibria could be formulated in the following fashion:

$$R_2M \cdot MZ_2 \cdot \text{solvent} \rightleftharpoons (RMZ)_n \text{ solvent} \rightleftharpoons R_2M \cdot \text{solvent} + MZ_2 \cdot \text{solvent} \qquad (3\text{-}3)$$

For synthetic purposes, such equilibria may often be manipulated, by proper choice of ligands and experimental conditions, in order to prepare either the symmetrical species, R_2M, or the unsymmetrical species, RMZ. Ligands that favor the redistribution to RMZ are usually groups of widely different polarity, such as R = alkyl or aryl and Z = halide or alkoxide.[24] For example, diethylgallium chloride can be prepared by heating two equivalents of triethylgallium and one equivalent of gallium chloride[25]:

$$2(CH_3CH_2)_3Ga + GaCl_3 \rightarrow 3(CH_3CH_2)_2GaCl \tag{3-4}$$

On the other hand, disproportionation to the symmetrical species can be achieved feasibly, even if the polarity of the groups on the metal is not very different. It suffices that the desired R_mM type be the most (or least) volatile species present in a rapidly equilibrating system; fractional distillation can then effect a good separation. The preparation of tri-*n*-decylgallium from

$$3(CH_3CH_2)_2(C_8H_{17}CH_2CH_2)Ga \rightarrow (C_8H_{17}CH_2CH_2)_3Ga + 2(CH_3CH_2)_3Ga \tag{3-5}$$

n-decyldiethylgallium (obtainable from 1-decene and diethylgallium hydride) can be achieved by the distillative removal of the more volatile triethylgallium (Eq. 3–5).[26] Other examples are the preparation of diethylzinc from ethylzinc iodide,[27] trimethylaluminum from methylaluminum sesquiiodide $[(CH_3)_3Al_2I_3]$,[28] and dimethylmagnesium from methylmagnesium chloride.[29]

An alternative method of driving the equilibrium in favor of the symmetrical types is that of precipitating one of the components. This process has two interesting aspects. In the first place, the question arises as to whether the symmetrical type thereby isolated was all formed from RMZ, or whether much or all of it pre-existed as a complex, $R_2M \cdot MZ_2$. The famous Schlenk equilibrium for Grignard reagents and all the controversy it has occasioned centers on this point. However, for the present, the formation of dialkylmagnesium in solution by the precipitation of magnesium halides (and alkyl magnesium halides) from Grignard reagents with dioxane $(C_4H_8O_2)$ can be interpreted in terms of such equilibria (Eq. 3–6).[30] The disproportionation

$$2RMgX + C_4H_8O_2 \rightarrow R_2Mg + MgX_2 \cdot C_4H_8O_2 \tag{3-6}$$

[24] (a) J. J. Eisch, *J. Am. Chem. Soc.*, **84**, 3830 (1962); (b) G. Calingaert and H. A. Beatty in *Organic Chemistry*, Vol. II (H. Gilman, ed.), Wiley, New York, 1943, pp. 1806–1820.

[25] J. J. Eisch, *J. Am. Chem. Soc.*, **84**, 3605 (1962).

[26] J. J. Eisch, *J. Am. Chem. Soc.*, **84**, 3830 (1962).

[27] C. R. Noller, *Organic Syntheses*, Vol. II (A. H. Blatt, ed.), Wiley, New York, 1943, p. 184.

[28] K. S. Pitzer and H. S. Gutowsky, *J. Am. Chem. Soc.*, **68**, 2204 (1946).

[29] H. Gilman and R. E. Brown, *Rec. trav. chim.*, **48**, 1133 (1929); **49**, 724 (1930).

[30] A sound précis of the copious, nonradioactive precipitation studies of the postulated Schlenk equilibrium is presented by M. S. Kharasch and O. Reinmuth, *Grignard Reactions of Nonmetallic Substances*, Prentice-Hall, Englewood Cliffs, N.J., 1954, pp. 99–109.

of alkylboron hydrides in the presence of amines[31] and of arylaluminum hydrides in the presence of ethyl ether[32] also illustrates the utility of precipitation for preparative purposes (Eqs. 3–7 and 3–8):

$$3(R_2BH)_2 + 4NR_3' \rightarrow 4R_3B:NR_3'\downarrow + B_2H_6\uparrow \qquad (3\text{-}7)$$

$$3(C_6H_5)_2AlH + OR_2' \rightarrow 2(C_6H_5)_3Al:OR_2' + (AlH_3)_n\downarrow \qquad (3\text{-}8)$$

In the second place, the behavior of alkyl derivatives of unstable metal valence states resembles precipitative disproportionation, in this case with the insoluble metal being one product. The alkyls of mercury(I), thallium(I), lead(II), and bismuth(I or II) owe their transitory existence to the rapidity of disproportionation:

$$R\text{—}Hg\text{—}Cl \xrightarrow{[H]} [R\text{—}Hg] \longrightarrow R_2Hg + Hg\downarrow \qquad (3\text{-}9)^{33}$$

$$3R\text{—}Tl \rightarrow R_3Tl + 2Tl\downarrow \qquad (3\text{-}10)^{34}$$

Surmise from the bridging nature of certain metal alkyls themselves (an equilibrated structure) leads to the hypothesis that group interchange (disproportionation or redistribution) with both associated metal alkyls and monomeric alkyls may proceed through a transition state involving bridging of the ligands to be exchanged (IX). Evidence in favor of such front-side or flank attack has come from a number of studies of group exchange. The formation of RHgX from R_2Hg and HgX_2 with the retention of optical

IX

activity in $R = R'R''R'''C$,[35] the disproportionation of $R_nR'_{3-n}B$ as catalyzed by boron hydrides or aluminum alkyls,[36] the aluminum chloride-catalyzed disproportionation of alkylchlorosilanes,[37] and many other data find a satisfactory interpretation only if transition states such as IX are invoked. The fact that the disproportionation of unassociated metal alkyls (as of silicon,

[31] R. Köster, *Angew. Chem.*, **69**, 94 (1957).
[32] (a) J. J. Eisch and W. C. Kaska, unpublished studies, 1963; (b) J. R. Surtees, *Chem. Ind.* (*London*), **1964**, 1260.
[33] B. G. Gowenlock and J. Trotman, *J. Chem. Soc.*, **1957**, 2114.
[34] H. Gilman and R. G. Jones, *J. Am. Chem. Soc.*, **61**, 1513 (1939); **62**, 2357 (1940).
[35] O. A. Reutov and E. V. Uglova, *Izv. Akad. Nauk SSSR Otd. Khim. Nauk*, 757 (1959); through *CA*, **53**, 21636 (1959).
[36] R. Köster and G. Bruno, *Ann.*, **629**, 89 (1960).
[37] R. O. Sauer and E. M. Hadsell, *J. Am. Chem. Soc.*, **70**, 3590 (1948).

boron, tin, etc.) is catalyzed by compounds able to bridge (BH_3, R_3Al, Lewis acids) supports a transition state in which two dissimilar metal centers (M and M') are involved. The more general implications of this will be considered later.

The foregoing intricate factors will have to be evaluated carefully both in specifying the nature of the equilibrium species present in RMZ and what the possible upsetting influence on the equilibria will be when the candidate reactant (R—C≡N, R_2C=O, R—CH=CH_2) is introduced. For example, once chemists are certain what the nature of the various Grignard reagents are, they will still have to proceed with caution in designating the kinetically significant species (any of the foregoing species or a new complex with the reactant) for individual Grignard reactions.

Shape of Molecular Units

The three-dimensional arrangement of atoms in the "molecular unit" would be expected to be a complex and variable situation, in light of the preceding comments on intramolecular and intermolecular association and solvation. The shape of organometallic molecules, both in solution and in the crystalline state, will determine the length and hence the polarity and steric accessibility of the carbon-metal bond. Up to the present, the crystal structures of several systems have been determined by X-ray analysis. The pioneering work of Rundle and coworkers has elucidated the structure of the tetra-methylplatinum tetramer,[13] the trimethylaluminum dimer,[1] the dimethyl-beryllium polymer,[5] the trimethylindium tetramer,[38] and, most recently, the phenylmagnesium bromide dietherate monomer.[39] In developing the bonding situation and hence the basis for molecular geometry in such electron-deficient systems the guiding principle appears to be that "delocalization of bonding occurs so as to use all the low-energy bonding orbitals of the metallic atom." The resulting bridge structures and their fate in donor solvents have been considered previously. Because of their central significance to synthesis and mechanism in organometallic chemistry, Grignard reagents have been the subject of numerous structural investigations in recent years. The structure of various Grignard reagents in solution has been attacked by a number of chemical and physical methods. The Schlenk equilibrium, postulated on the basis of the precipitation of magnesium bromide by dioxane, recently has come in and out of vogue with the rapidity of a revolving door. The identity in behavior between the conventional ethylmagnesium bromide prepared from ethyl bromide and magnesium in ethyl ether and ethereal mixtures of diethyl-

[38] E. L. Amma and R. E. Rundle, *J. Am. Chem. Soc.*, **80**, 4141 (1958).
[39] G. D. Stucky and R. E. Rundle, *J. Am. Chem. Soc.*, **85**, 1002 (1963).

magnesium and magnesium bromide was based upon kinetic behavior toward 1-alkynes, conductance measurements, and dielectric constant.[40] Moreover, mixing $Mg^{28}Br_2$ with $(CH_3CH_2)_2Mg$ in ether solution and reprecipitating the magnesium bromide gave only 6–8% exchange.[41a] This finding appeared to dismiss the Schlenk equilibrium (Eq. 3–11) as a necessary description of Grignard reagents in ethyl ether solution. Later exchange studies with the more stable $Mg^{25}Br_2$ by two independent research groups found statistical exchange.[41b, c] Electrolytic deposition of magnesium from similar mixtures for the ethyl and the phenyl case [42] likewise led to the conclusion that there was no exchange of magnesium and hence the species RMgBr was dismissed from possible Grignard equilibria:

$$2RMgBr \rightleftharpoons R_2Mg \cdot MgBr_2 \rightleftharpoons R_2Mg + MgBr_2 \qquad (3\text{--}11)$$

The complex $R_2Mg \cdot MgX_2$ and hence the structure X were favored in view of the dimeric character of the Grignard reagent in ether and the previous isolation of crystalline dietherates. However, the existence of the species

X

RMgX in certain solvents receives support from the observation that ethylmagnesium chloride is monomeric in tetrahydrofuran and that again a mixture of diethylmagnesium and magnesium chloride exhibits the same behavior as the Grignard reagent. Fractional crystallization produced a quantitative precipitation of $[(CH_3CH_2)Mg_2Cl_3]_n$ and left behind a solution of $(CH_3CH_2)_2Mg$ [presumably $n = 1$; if $n = 2$, this precipitate could be $(CH_3CH_2)_2Mg \cdot 3MgCl_2$]. These data are interpreted to mean that exchange must take place between $(CH_3CH_2)_2Mg$ and $MgCl_2$, and hence the original Schlenk equilibrium is still an important description of Grignard systems, with CH_3CH_2MgCl being the important species.[43] Thus, in ether solution where such reagents are dimeric, structure XI is favored. The situation has now been

XI

[40] (a) R. E. Dessy, J. H. Wotiz, and C. A. Hollingsworth, *J. Am. Chem. Soc.*, **79**, 358 (1957); (b) R. E. Dessy and R. M. Jones, *J. Org. Chem.*, **24**, 1685 (1959).

[41] (a) R. E. Dessy, G. S. Handler, J. H. Wotiz, and C. A. Hollingsworth, *J. Am. Chem. Soc.*, **79**, 3476 (1957); (b) R. E. Dessy, S. E. I. Green, and R. M. Salinger, *Tetrahedron Letters*, **1964** (21), 1369; (c) D. O. Cowan, J. Hsu, and J. D. Roberts, *J. Org. Chem.*, **29**, 3688 (1964).

[42] R. E. Dessy and G. S. Handler, *J. Am. Chem. Soc.*, **80**, 5824 (1958).

[43] E. C. Ashby and W. E. Becker, *J. Am. Chem. Soc.*, **85**, 118 (1963).

made even more formidable by the recent X-ray study of solid phenyl-magnesium bromide isolated from ethyl ether. Monomeric units of magnesium bonded tetrahedrally to bromine, phenyl, and two ether molecules have been discerned in the solid state.[39] Although extrapolation of such data to the solution state is fraught with uncertainties, it is felt that such monomeric units are an adequate explanation for this case also, since this Grignard tends to form polymeric structures when the ether:magnesium ratio falls below 2:1. Hence, the bridge structure discussed above is unsuitable. But this neglects the findings of Ubbelohde and others to the effect that phenyl- and aryl-magnesium bromides are at least dimeric in ether and that higher degrees of association can be observed under certain conditions.[44] Although similar ambiguities exist in elucidating the precise structure of associated metal alkyls of Groups IA containing alkali metal halides, a clearing picture is emerging for salt-free lithium alkyls. The physical state and the nature of the solvent medium exercise decisive structural influences. Thus, mass spectrometric data support the occurrence of tetrameric and hexameric ethyllithium in the vapor state[45a]; in hydrocarbon media ethyllithium seems to exist largely as a hexamer[45b] and *t*-butyllithium as a tetramer[45c]; and in the solid state ethyllithium is known to array itself in a tetrahedron of lithium centers with bridging methylene groups.[45d] Donor solvents such as tertiary amines and ethers are known to effect a depolymerization of the associated species,[45e] and evidence has been presented that butyllithium persists in ethyl ether as a dimeric monoetherate.[45f, g] Thus with both Grignard and organolithium reagents structural specification is a humbling, onerous task not conducive to broad generalizations.

With nonassociated metal alkyls the specification of structure in solution might appear to follow from X-ray or electron diffraction data gathered on pure samples. Such a conclusion generally is not warranted. The trigonal coplanarity of trimethylborane in the gas phase almost certainly becomes tetrahedral in highly donor media such as trimethylamine.[46] With the exception of tetramethylplatinum, the structure of σ-bonded transition metal alkyls has received little attention. The observation that transition metal alkyls undergo rapid decomposition to free metal and hydrocarbons in ether, but are much more stable as complexes in donor media, suggests different stereochemistry for the metal alkyls in different environments. The effect of

[44] W. Slough and A. R. Ubbelohde, *J. Chem. Soc.*, **1955**, 108.

[45] (a) J. Berkowitz, D. A. Bafus, and T. L. Brown, *J. Phys. Chem.*, **65**, 1380 (1961); (b) T. L. Brown, D. W. Dickerhoof, and D. A. Bafus, *J. Am. Chem. Soc.*, **84**, 1371 (1962); (c) M. Weiner, G. Vogel, and R. West, *Inorg. Chem.*, **1**, 654 (1962); (d) H. Dietrich, *Acta Cryst.*, **16**, 681 (1963); (e) T. L. Brown, R. L. Gerteis, D. A. Bafus, and J. A. Ladd, *J. Am. Chem. Soc.*, **86**, 2135 (1964); (f) J. F. Eastham and G. W. Gibson, *ibid.*, **85**, 2171 (1963); (g) Z. K. Cheema, G. W. Gibson, and J. F. Eastham, *ibid.*, **85**, 3571 (1963).

[46] A. B. Burg and A. A. Green, *J. Am. Chem. Soc.*, **65**, 1838 (1943).

donor ligands upon the structure of transition metal organometallics is illustrated by the following coordination compounds of *cis-* and *trans-*diarylplatinum(II),[47] alkylgold(I),[48] and triarylchromium(III) (XII–XIV)[49]:

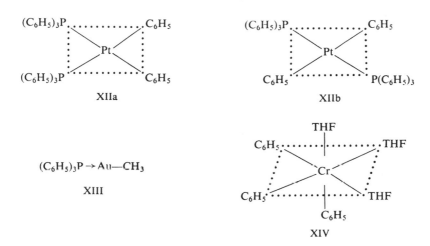

(C₆H₅)₃P → Au—CH₃

XIII

Molecular Shape and Facile Isomerizations

Just as ambiguity exists with Grignard reagents as to the distribution and lability of the carbon-magnesium linkages, many other organometallic compounds may undergo facile isomerization. Carbon-metal linkages with acetylenic, vinyl, and allyl groups are especially labile. With substituted vinylic and allylic moieties, the organometallic compound R—M can undergo *cis-trans* and allylic isomerizations, producing a new structure R'—M. The nature of the metal seems to determine the ease of isomerization; the structures of R and R' largely determine the equilibrium point between the isomers. Of special interest here are isomerization mechanisms peculiar to the organometallic systems. The more general chemical implications of isomerization will be considered in a later chapter.

The steric stability of vinylmetallic derivatives can have profound influence on physical properties. Relatively little is known about the pathways by which such isomerization can occur. *A posteriori*, a bridging association of vinyl groups might lower the rotational barrier about the vinyl linkage, thus permitting isomerization of *cis-*vinylmetallic derivatives[17] to *trans-*vinyl derivatives (XV). Or a solvent-separated ion-pair formation with subsequent

[47] J. Chatt and B. L. Shaw, *J. Chem. Soc.*, **1959**, 4020.
[48] G. Calvin, G. E. Coates, and P. S. Dixon, *Chem. Ind.* (*London*), **1959**, 1628.
[49] W. Herwig and H. Zeiss, *J. Am. Chem. Soc.*, **79**, 6561 (1957); **81**, 4891 (1959).

$$\text{XV}$$

inversion could be pictured (Eq. 3–12).[50] Finally, catalysts capable of adding to the double bond reversibly could effect isomerization via an addition-elimination. Promotion of the isomerization of vinyllithium compounds by the use of donor solvents (B:) seems to favor a mechanism similar to that of Eq. 3–12,[50] while the thermal behavior of vinylaluminum adducts points to an addition-elimination isomerization (Eq. 3–13)[51]:

$$(3\text{–}12)$$

$$(3\text{–}13)$$

Similar concern for the real structure of allylic organometallic compounds has centered around the point(s) of attachment of the metal atom on the allyl system. The possible equilibrium between isomeric species (XVI) versus a postulated bridge (XVII) scheme has been put to an n.m.r. test. Thus, since

$$\text{XVIa} \qquad \text{XVIb} \qquad \text{XVII}$$

both allylmagnesium bromide[52] and allyllithium[53] in ether solution yield proton doublet and quintet signals, a very rapid equilibration between XVIa and XVIb (R = H) must take place or a bridged monomer (or dimer) must be present. However, the changing character of the n.m.r. spectrum of the Grignard reagent prepared from γ,γ-dimethylallyl bromide over a tempera-

[50] D. Y. Curtin and W. J. Koehl, *J. Am. Chem. Soc.*, **84**, 1967 (1962).
[51] J. J. Eisch and W. C. Kaska, *J. Am. Chem. Soc.*, **85**, 2165 (1963).
[52] J. E. Nordlander and J. D. Roberts, *J. Am. Chem. Soc.*, **81**, 1769 (1959).
[53] C. S. Johnson, Jr., M. A. Weiner, J. S. Waugh, and D. Seyferth, *J. Am. Chem. Soc.*, **83** 1306 (1961).

ture range suggests that the time averaging of the methyl protons is frozen out at lower temperatues, leading to two nonequivalent methyl groups. This rules out structures whose methyl groups would be unchanging and also supports the view that the Grignard reagent exists almost exclusively as the primary isomer (R = CH$_3$).[54] In an extension of such a conclusion, the ultraviolet comparison of cinnamylmagnesium bromide with styryl model compounds supports the predominant existence of the primary isomer (R = C$_6$H$_5$, R = H) also.[55] It might be mentioned that although the allylic derivatives of the alkali and alkaline earth metals seem best represented by a dynamic equilibration of structures XVIa and XVIb, the bridging structure XVII is realized with transition metal derivatives. In certain of these cases the borderline between σ- and π-bonded organometallic compounds merges. Bis-π-allylnickel exists as a mixture of isomeric sandwich structures (XVIIIa and XVIIIb)[56]:

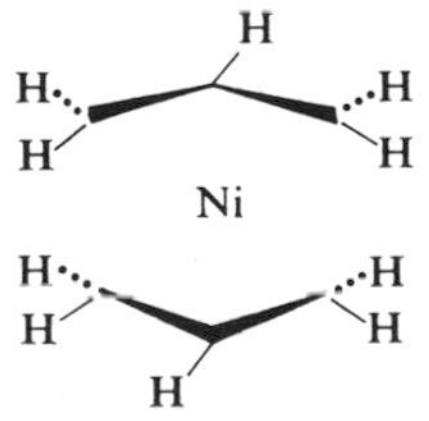

XVIIIa

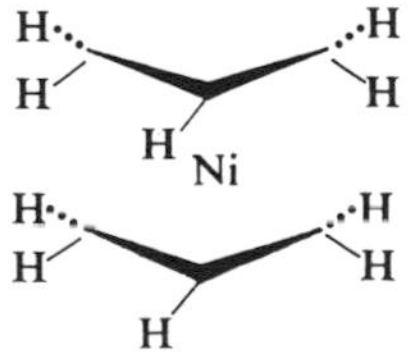

XVIIIb

[54] G. M. Whitesides, J. E. Nordlander, and J. D. Roberts, *J. Am. Chem. Soc.*, **84**, 2010 (1962).

[55] R. H. DeWolfe, D. L. Hagmann, and W. G. Young, *J. Am. Chem. Soc.*, **79**, 4795 (1957).

[56] (a) G. Wilke and B. Bogdanovic, *Angew. Chem.*, **73**, 756 (1961); (b) R. F. Heck and D. S. Breslow, *J. Am. Chem. Soc.*, **83**, 1097 (1961); (c) H. B. Jonassen, R. I. Stearns, J. Kentämaa, D. W. Moore, and A. G. Whittaker, *ibid.*, **80**, 2586 (1958).

FOUR
Nature of Carbon-Metal Bonding

Bond Polarity and Electronegativity

The variety of structure exhibited by organometallic compounds certainly stems from the bonding differences of the some eighty elements involved in carbon-metal bonds. Even if the organometallic π-complexes of the transition metals are excepted from this discussion of ionic and covalent σ carbon-metal bonds, a comprehensive description of such bonding is a task worthy of Sisyphus. For not only must the thermodynamic stability, possible π- and σ-character, and geometry of existing metal alkyls be accommodated in an acceptable theory, but also their chemical reactivity and indeed the non-existence of certain transition metal organometallics require an explanation. With an anxious eye on the torrent of new experimental findings, this writer hastens to disclaim being a Sisyphus. He will be pleased if he can identify the boulders and the hills.

Possibly the most straightforward description of carbon-metal bonding is in terms of its polarity. The saline or ionic alkyls of rubidium and cesium might be viewed as a most extreme example having electrostatic bonding. Even here the bonding situation is not simple, for recent evidence has been obtained on the existence of both contact ion pairs and solvent-separated ion pairs for alkali metal derivatives of fluorene in solution.[1] Borderline organometalloids, such as boron and selenium alkyls, form the other limit where

[1] T. E. Hogan-Esch and J. Smid, *J. Am. Chem. Soc.*, **88**, 307, 318 (1966).

50

very little polar character is involved in the covalent carbon-element bond. Since the electronegativity of carbon would not be expected to change too markedly in its different organic groups R, the polarity of the carbon-metal bond is determined largely by the metal. In correlating structural and chemical properties with bond polarity, a most useful parameter in preliminary discussions is the electronegativity (X). Although several individually consistent scales of electron-attracting abilities have been devised, the electronegativity values of Allred and Rochow[2] have the advantages of wide availability for most elements and of empirical consistency. On the basis of the electro-

negativity values given in Table 4–1, the bond polarity, $\overset{\delta-}{C}$—$\overset{\delta+}{M}$, should increase as the electronegativity index X decreases. Being an empirical parameter composed of several atomic variables, electronegativity itself is not suitable for a complete electronic discussion of structure and reactivity. Later considerations will show the great importance of available metal orbitals, steric factors, and the nature of the reaction.

TABLE 4–1

Allred-Rochow Electronegativities of Metallic Elements

Fr	0.86	Ta	1.33	Cr	1.56
Cs	0.86	Pd	1.35	Mn	1.60
Rb	0.89	Tc	1.36	Fe	1.64
K	0.91	W	1.40	Zn	1.66
Li	0.97	Ru	1.42	Bi	1.67
Ra	0.97	Au	1.42	Co	1.70
Ba	0.97	Ag	1.42	Sn	1.72
Sr	0.99	Pt	1.44	Si	1.74
Na	1.01	Hg	1.44	Ni	1.75
Ca	1.04	Tl	1.44	Cu	1.75
Lanthanides	1.01–1.14	V	1.45	Ga	1.82
Actinides	1.00–1.2	Rh	1.45	Sb	1.82
Y	1.11	Cd	1.46	At	1.96
Sc	1.20	Re	1.46	B	2.01
Zr	1.22	Be	1.47	Te	2.01
Mg	1.23	Al	1.47	Ge	2.02
Hf	1.23	In	1.49	P	2.06
Nb	1.23	Os	1.52	As	2.20
Mo	1.30	Ir	1.55	I	2.21
Ti	1.32	Pb	1.55	Se	2.48
				C	*2.50*

As to correlations between electronegativity and structure or reactivity, it appears that metal alkyls tend to be saline in character when $X_M \leqslant 1.0$ and

---

[2] (a) A. L. Allred and E. G. Rochow, *J. Inorg. Nucl. Chem.*, **5**, 264, 269 (1958); (b) A. L. Allred, *ibid.*, **17**, 215 (1961).

to be associated in solution or in the pure state when $X_M \leqslant 1.5$. But the limitations of purely an ionic treatment of organometallic structure were examined in Chapter Three. Despite these limitations, however, electronegativity is of considerable help in discerning trends in chemical reactivity. The very exceptions to such reactivity rules can themselves lend great insight into the detailed electronic reaction mechanism. The most general reagents for organometallic substrates appear to be halogen, protic acids, and molecular oxygen. Organometallics of all the metals in Table 4–1 respond to these reagents, except for the inertness of Group IVA and mercury alkyls toward oxygen.[3] By and large, the reactivity to more discriminating substrates increases as the electronegativity of the metal decreases. The empirically established reactivity rules of Gilman and coworkers provide ample support for the parallelism between carbon-metal bond polarity and chemical reactivity.[4] The fruits of many detailed mechanistic studies now permit these broad generalizations to be assessed in more fundamental terms. The importance of experimental conditions in determining relative reactivities of metal alkyls is now apparent, and these newer views will be discussed in succeeding sections.

With a given metal the nature of the organic group R can have a significant influence on the reactivity of the carbon-metal bond. The effect is not nearly as large as that of the metal's nature. Therefore, one would wish to compile electronegativity parameters for organic groups, or at least to assess the ability of R to hold a negative charge. The polarity of a bond, $\overset{\delta-}{R}\!-\!\overset{\delta+}{M}$, under a given polarizing field of M, will depend upon the anionic stability of the carbon as $R^{\ominus}M^{\oplus}$. A semiquantitative order for the electron-attracting power of R might result from estimating the acidities of the hydrocarbons, R—H. The more acidic R—H is, the more electron-attracting $R^{\ominus}$ will be. A number of experimental methods has sought to order carbanionic stabilities. Early studies of equilibrium constants for competitive metalations with saline organometallics,[5] recent work on iodine-lithium interconversions,[6] and both electrochemical and magnesium-mercury exchange reactions with organomercurials[7] have led to a concordant ordering of carbanion stabilities.

[3] It should be noted that the carbon-metal bond of Group VA alkyls is not always cleaved by these reagents; rather, adducts of the type R_3MZ ($Z = O$, X_2) are formed. In the case of transition metal alkyls, many metals have not yielded stable alkyl derivatives. Hence, the chemical behavior of their R_mM types can only be surmised.

[4] Cf. H. Gilman in *Organic Chemistry*, Vol. I (H. Gilman, ed.), Wiley, New York, 1943, pp. 520–524, for the classical rules which imposed badly needed order upon the chaos of reactivity speculation.

[5] (a) J. B. Conant and G. W. Wheland, *J. Am. Chem. Soc.*, **54**, 1212 (1932); (b) W. K. McEwen, *ibid.*, **58**, 1124 (1936).

[6] D. E. Applequist and D. F. O'Brien, *J. Am. Chem. Soc.*, **85**, 743 (1963).

[7] R. E. Dessy, W. Kitching, T. Psarras, R. Salinger, A. Chen, and T. Chivers, *J. Am. Chem. Soc.*, **88**, 460 (1966).

Apparently in all cases the more electronegative R group allies itself preferentially with the less electronegative metal (Eq. 4–1):

$$R—M + R'—M' \rightleftharpoons R—M' + R'—M$$

$$R = C_6H_5 \quad R' = CH_3 \quad M = HgR, I, H \quad M' = MgR', Li, Na$$

(4–1)

Recast in terms of pK_a values of the hydrocarbon, R—H, this sequence of carbanionic stabilities is given in Table 4–2.[8] The smaller the pK_a of R—H, the more electron attracting $R^\ominus$ will be. As with the electronegativity values of the metals, these pK_a values are composites of several electronic factors. A general analysis into inductive, resonance, and steric factors will be undertaken later in this chapter.

TABLE 4–2

Relative Carbanion Stabilities of Organic Groups[a]

Group R	pK_a of R—H	
Cyclopentyl	44	
Isopropyl	43	
n-Propyl	41	
Ethyl	40.5	
Methyl	39	
Cyclopropyl	38	
Vinyl	37	increasing
Phenyl	37	anionic
Allyl	36.5	stability
Benzyl	35	
Diphenylmethyl	33	
Triphenylmethyl	31	
Fluorenyl (9)	27	
Indenyl (3)	23	
Phenylethynyl	18.5	
Cyclopentadienyl	18	

[a] R. E. Dessy et al., *J. Am. Chem. Soc.*, **88**, 460 (1966).

To a first approximation, then, enhanced polarity of the carbon-metal bond might be expected as the electronegativity of the metal decreases and the carbanionic stability of $R_1R_2R_3C^\ominus$ increases. Now, in the reactions of

[8] D. J. Cram, *Fundamentals of Carbanion Chemistry*, Benjamin, New York, 1965, p. 19.

organometallics with polar substrates, Y—Z, a formidable body of evidence supports a synchronous four-center (I) or six-center transition state (II) for

I   II

the carbon-metal bond cleavage.[9] In such a representation, it is understandable why bond polarity should influence reactivity. However, reactivities of organometallics of a given metal do not always increase with the carbanion stability of R. This is a warning that reaction mechanism is not explained solely by bond polarities.

Electronic and Nuclear Factors of the Metal

The gross electronegativity as a measure of heteropolar carbon-metal bonding embraces a number of atomic parameters. First, there is the nuclear charge. Within a period of the periodic table, increasing nuclear charge (atomic number Z) for successive elements results in a decreasing polarity in the C—M linkage. As an illustration, consider the alkyls of sodium, magnesium, and aluminum. In families of metals, on the other hand, the increasing nuclear charge on the metal center does not always result in a diminished C—M bond polarity of the alkyl derivatives. Although this is true for alkyls of Groups IIIA and IVA, one finds the polarity of C—M bonds with alkali and alkaline earth alkyls actually increasing as the metal families are descended. In the latter cases the effective nuclear charge is actually less with the heavier members because of screening by filled electronic orbitals. Thus, alkyls of cesium are much more saline than those of lithium.

Second, many lines of evidence demonstrate that residual bonding capacity is important in organometallic structure and chemical behavior. The general Lewis acid character of metal alkyls can be ascribed to the availability of low-energy, unoccupied electronic orbitals in the metal center. For the alkyls of Groups IA, IIA, IIIA, and the transition metal series, this Lewis acidity could involve the *np*-orbitals. With the metalloids of Groups IVA–VIIA and certain transition metal alkyls, the *n* or *n* − 1 *d*-orbitals might be employed. On the basis of Lewis acidity strength, the metal center in R—M has an increasing tendency to accept electron pairs (from amines, ethers, and halide ions,

[9] R. E. Dessy and F. Paulik, *J. Chem. Educ.*, **40**, 185 (1963).

inter alia) as one goes from left to right in a given period (RNa < R_2Mg < R_3Al)[10] and one ascends a given family (R_3Tl < R_3In < R_3Ga < R_3Al).[11]

As the former coordination compounds would reasonably involve the np orbitals of the metal, the question of the Lewis acidity of metal centers having d-orbitals is also of interest. With transition metal organometallics, the $n-1$ d-orbitals can form hybridized orbitals with ns-, and np-orbitals having strong bonding properties. But a detailed consideration of coordination complexes would be too extensive to undertake here.[12] Suffice it to point out that in forming Lewis complexes with bases like R_2O, R_2S, R_3P, R_3As, RO^-, and X^-, the transition metal alkyl often gains considerably in over-all stability. Since the increase in kinetic or thermodynamic stability may mean that R_mM (Lewis base) can be isolated while R_mM is too unstable to exist, it is hard to order transition metal alkyls R_mM according to Lewis acid strength. This stabilization of a transition metal alkyl or aryl by coordination with suitable ligands is a valuable aid in synthesis. Such "conditioning" of a valence state for good bonding is thought to involve rehybridization of orbitals, so that the energy difference is increased between the lowest antibonding M.O. and the highest bonding M.O. For it is believed that electron promotion between such M.O. is partially responsible for thermal decomposition.[13] Clearly steric interference with the approach of the reagent to the metal-carbon bond can also contribute to a heightened chemical stability.

With main group alkyls of Groups IVA–VIA, the available orbitals are believed to be nd-orbitals. Gradations in Lewis acidity among these alkyl derivatives cannot be assessed by equilibrium measurements. In general, no stable complexes of R_mM with Lewis bases have been observed, although some mixed types (RMX_{m-1}) are Lewis acids. On the other hand, much kinetic and stereochemical evidence on the cleavage of carbon-metalloid bonds by nucleophiles (OH^-, R^-, H^-) tends to implicate d-orbital participation in the transition state (III).[14] Trends of d-orbital involvement within a given family probably would be obscured by factors such as bond strength and steric accessibility.

A third aspect of metal bonding is that the metal center in an organometallic might behave as an electron source or as an electron sink for unsaturated groups attached to it. Both electronic interactions are ascribed to metal d-orbitals. The filled transition metal $n-1$ d-orbitals of proper symmetry are proposed to overlap with the available antibonding π-orbitals of attached carbonyl, vinyl, and phenyl groups. Such back-bonding serves to disperse

---

[10] G. Wittig, *Angew. Chem.*, **70**, 65 (1958).

[11] G. E. Coates and R. A. Whitcombe, *J. Chem. Soc.*, **1956**, 3351.

[12] Cf., *inter alia*, F. A. Cotton and G. Wilkinson, *Advanced Inorganic Chemistry*, Wiley (Interscience), New York, 1962, pp. 560–610.

[13] J. Chatt and B. L. Shaw, *J. Chem. Soc.*, **1959**, 705, 4020.

[14] C. Eaborn, *Organosilicon Compounds*, Academic, New York, 1960, pp. 103–113.

the accumulated negative charge on the metal and to enhance the electron density between the metal and carbon centers. The structure of pentafluorophenylmanganese pentacarbonyl in IV depicts this situation. Here strong

III   IV

inductive withdrawal of electrons in the σ-carbon-manganese bond by C_6F_5 is also important in stabilizing the compound (cf. *infra*). This so-called d_π—p_π bonding by a metal donor, significant in many transition metal alkyls and aryls, explains why unsaturated groups with electronegative substituents form stable C—M bonds. The compounds $(C_6H_5)_3Cr(C_4H_8O)_3$,[15] $C_6H_5Ti(O-i-C_3H_7)_3$,[16] and $Na_2[Ni(C{\equiv}C—R)_4]$[17] exemplify this rule.

The converse electronic effect, the donation of π-electrons by unsaturated groups attached to the metal, is of great current interest. This interaction could be viewed as p_π—p_π or d_π—p_π bonding, depending upon the availability and energy of metal orbitals. Although the significance of such supplemental bonding remains a moot question in many cases, the alkyls of Group III and the higher valence states of transition metals might participate in p_π—p_π bonding. The reduced Lewis acidity and the inertness toward oxygen of trivinylborane[18] (V) are suggestive of p_π—p_π delocalization.[19] In the case of organometalloids of Groups IVA–VIA, the absence of primary p_π—p_π

$$(H_2C{=}CH)_2B{-}\overset{H}{C}{=}CH_2 \leftrightarrow (H_2C{=}CH)_2B{\overset{\ominus}{=}}\overset{H}{C}{\overset{\oplus}{-}}CH_2$$

V

[15] W. Herwig and H. H. Zeiss, *J. Am. Chem. Soc.*, **79**, 656 (1957).
[16] D. F. Herman and W. K. Nelson, *J. Am. Chem. Soc.*, **75**, 3877 (1953).
[17] R. Nast, K. Vester, and H. Griesshammer, *Ber.*, **90**, 2678 (1957).
[18] (a) T. D. Parsons and D. M. Ritter, *J. Am. Chem. Soc.*, **76**, 1710 (1954); (b) T. D. Parsons, M. B. Silverman, and D. M. Ritter, *ibid.*, **79**, 5091 (1957).
[19] Cf. T. D. Coyle, S. L. Stafford, and F. G. A. Stone, *J. Chem. Soc.*, **1961**, 3103, for an appraisal of chemical and spectroscopic evidence of π-character in organoboranes.

bonding is evidenced in all their molecular structures. However, the spectroscopic[20] and chemical[21, 22] properties of vinylsilanes, for example, support the importance of d_π—p_π secondary bonding in the ground state (VI) and in the transition states[23] (VII) of these systems. Data are accumulating from other vinylmetalloids suggesting the operation of d_π—p_π bonding. Theoretical

calculations of *d*-orbital π-bonding, using overlap integrals as criteria of bond strength, have reached the conclusion that such bonding should be significant in many transition metal and main group compounds.[24]

A fourth important metal atom parameter is its covalent radius. In itself this value is a compromise between the nuclear charge's attraction for its electron cloud and the repulsion between like charges on separate nuclei. The resulting carbon-metal bond lengths (Table 4–4) can have two straightforward effects on chemical reactivity. With first-period metals (Li, Be, B) the small metal radius may impede many chemical reactions at the carbon-metal bond because of steric hindrance. The longer bond lengths of main group metals of higher atomic number result in lower bond strengths. Consequently, carbon bonds to mercury, thallium, and lead will be chemically very labile.

Electronic and Steric Factors of the Organic Moiety

The stability conferred on the carbon-metal bond in R—M depends upon the unsaturation of R and its location. Carbon-carbon unsaturation α,β or β,γ with respect to the C—M linkage is most significant. For α,β-unsaturation the stability of the potential carbanion in R—M parallels the assumed hybridization of the α-carbon atom (cf. Table 4–1). In the following series stability increases as the *s*-character of the α-carbon increases:

[20] (a) J. J. Eisch and J. T. Trainor, *J. Org. Chem.*, **28**, 487 (1963); (b) R. Summitt, J. J. Eisch, J. T. Trainor, and M. T. Rogers, *J. Phys. Chem.*, **67**, 2367 (1963).
[21] C. Eaborn, *Organosilicon Compounds*, Academic, New York, 1960, pp. 103–113.
[22] J. J. Eisch and R. J. Beuhler, *J. Org. Chem.*, **28**, 2876 (1963).
[23] J. J. Eisch and G. R. Husk, *J. Org. Chem.*, **29**, 254 (1964).
[24] D. P. Craig, A. Maccoll, R. S. Nyholm, L. E. Orgel, and L. E. Sutton, *J. Chem. Soc.*, **1954**, 332.

$$R—CH_2—M < R—CH{=}CH—M \simeq C_6H_5—M < R—C{\equiv}C—M$$
$$\quad sp^3 \qquad\qquad sp^2 \qquad\qquad sp^2 \qquad\qquad sp$$

The lessened shielding of the carbon nucleus with enhanced *s*-character means that σ-electron density at the carbon will be higher. This situation is reflected in the increased saline character of metal acetylides over metal alkenyls and of metal aryls over metal alkyls. Since the acidity of the corresponding hydrocarbon R—H will increase as the stability of $R^\ominus$ increases, these stability considerations will be especially important in transmetalation reactions. Now that ^{13}C—H n.m.r. coupling constants have been proposed as an experimental measure of *s*-character [25] (Table 4–3), hydrocarbon acidity may reasonably be assessed from spectroscopic data. The facile metalation of

TABLE 4–3

^{13}C–H N.M.R., Spin-Spin Coupling Constants

Compound	$J_{^{13}C—H}$ (c.p.s.)	% *s*-Character of C—H bond	Ref.
$C(CH_3)_4$	120	25	a
(cyclohexene C—H)	170	33.3	a
(benzene C—H)	159	31.5	a
$CH_3—C{\equiv}C—H$	248	50	a
Cyclopropane	161	32	b
Cyclobutane	134	27	b
Cyclopentane	128	26	b
Cyclohexane	124	25	b
Cyclodecane	118	24	b
(dimethyl cyclopropene)	220	44	c

^{a} J. N. Shoolery, *J. Chem. Phys.*, **31**, 1427 (1963).
^{b} C. S. Foote, *Tetrahedron Letters*, **1963**, 579.
^{c} G. L. Closs, *Proc. Chem. Soc.*, **1962**, 152.

[25] (a) J. N. Shoolery, *J. Chem. Phys.*, **31**, 1427 (1963); (b) C. S. Foote, *Tetrahedron Letters*, **1963**, 579.

3,3-dimethylcyclopropene by methyllithium to yield the 1-cyclopropenyl-lithium [26] correlates with the 44% s-character of the vinyl hydrogens.

   The foregoing discussion of carbanionic stability implies that the reactivity of saline alkyls will run in a reverse order. It is true that reactivity decreases, alkyl > vinyl > acetylenic. However, noteworthy is the fact that with covalent metal alkyls, the reactivity order is usually reversed: acetylenic and vinyl > alkyl. A general discussion of reactivity of RM as a function of unsaturation in R seems appropriate, therefore.

   As with α,β-unsaturation in R—M, β,γ-unsaturation can cause an increase or decrease of chemical stability, depending upon the nature of the metal. Such β,γ-unsaturated systems include metal derivatives of the allylic, benzylic, or propargylic types, as well C—M bonds adjacent to carbonyl, nitro, or azomethine linkages. Among the alkali metals, where a saline structure obtains for the organometallic, such β,γ-unsaturated derivatives are decidedly less reactive than their metal alkyls. Allylic and related derivatives of covalent metal alkyl type, on the other hand, exhibit a chemical reactivity surpassing that of the saturated types. A common explanation of the reactivity for both α,β- and β,γ-unsaturated types can be advanced. With saline derivatives the structure of the ground state of R—M can be represented as a cluster of ions. The stabilization of $R^\ominus$ by increased electronegativity (increased s-character) with vinyl, phenyl, or acetylenic groups, or by π-electron delocalization with allylic types (VIII), would diminish the nucleophilicity of this anion. It is understandable why such an anion should be less reactive than a carbanion localized on saturated carbon; such ground-state stabilization increases its activation energy (E_2) relative to the saturated type E_1 (Figure 1). In contrast,

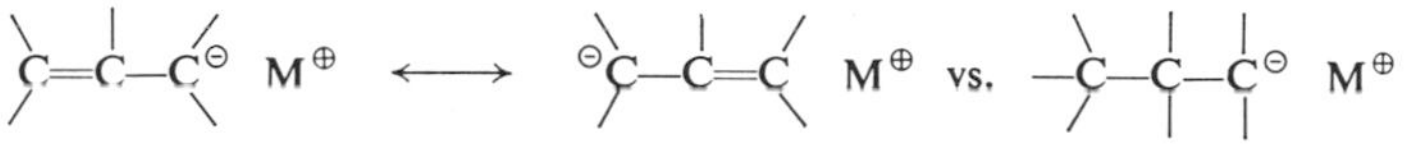

VIII

the ground-state stabilization of covalent organometallics is less pronounced, since the C—M bond has less ionic character. However, the heterolysis of this bond in the transition state should be aided by the reorganization energy for allylic types (Figure 2) and by the π-electron assistance to electrophilic attack (IXa, Z = H^+, X^+, R^+) for vinyl and acetylenic types, or S_E2' processes (IXb) for allylic systems. Hence, the over-all activation energy E_4 should be

IXa   IXb

[26] G. L. Closs, *Proc. Chem. Soc.*, **1962**, 152.

lowered relative to the saturated type (E_3) and a greater reactivity would be the result.

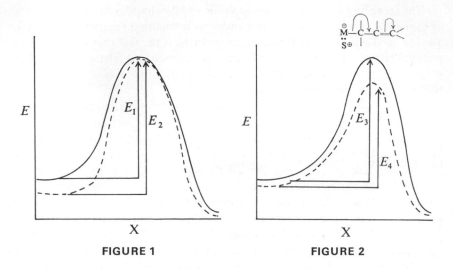

FIGURE 1   FIGURE 2

The greater reactivity of allylmagnesium bromide over n-propylmagnesium bromide in additions to the C=N bond of benzophenone anil illustrates the effect of β,γ-unsaturation in covalent metal alkyls.[27] In addition, although trialkylboranes are most resistant to hydrolysis, triallylborane hydrolyzes readily.[28]

The steric demands of organometallic reagents are undoubtedly important, but careful studies with well-defined systems are rare. Much of such research has involved Grignard reagents, whose structure and mode of solvation is still a moot question. In Chapter Three it was seen that highly branched R groups tended to promote the existence of associated alkyls $(R—M)_X$ as monomers. Hence, since the monomer would often be the kinetically significant species in reaction mechanisms, bulky monomeric metal alkyls may occasionally be more reactive than straight-chain, associated types. The lower reactivity of associated methyllithium and trimethyl-aluminum, in comparison with ethyl analogs, may serve as an illustration. For unassociated, covalent metal alkyls cleavage studies suggest that in cases where a synchronous, four-center transition state is involved,[9] the steric shielding of the carbon-metal bond can play a role (X). In his studies on the competitive cleavage of mixed dialkylmercurys, R—Hg—R', by HCl in inert

[27] H. Gilman and J. Eisch, *J. Am. Chem. Soc.*, **79**, 2150 (1957).
[28] B. M. Mikhailov and F. B. Tutorskaya, *Dokl. Akad. Nauk SSSR*, **123**, 479 (1958); through *C.A.*, **53**, 6990 (1959).

$$R_2 \diagdown \overset{\displaystyle R_1}{\underset{\displaystyle R_3 \diagup}{C}} - M$$

$$Y - Z$$

$$X$$

solvents, Kharasch found cleavage of R or R′ favored in the descending order.

$$CH_3 > C_2H_5 > n\text{-}C_3H_7 > i\text{-}C_3H_7 > t\text{-}C_4H_9 \;^{29}$$

Even though this fits a picture of steric hindrance, attention should be directed to more recent independent rate measurements where

$$C_2H_5 \gg i\text{-}C_3H_7 > n\text{-}Pr > CH_3 \;^{30}$$

However, in cleavage reactions of a redox, solvolytic character the loss of a metal (mercury) in a lower oxidation state leaves the organic group with considerable carbonium ion character (XI).[31] It is then understandable why *t*-butyl and isopropyl groups become so markedly reactive as steric retardation is overcome.

$$R_2 \diagdown \overset{\displaystyle R_1}{\underset{\displaystyle R_3 \diagup}{C}^{\oplus}} \cdots Hg^{\circ} \cdots OTs^{\ominus}$$

$$XI$$

Function of the Medium

The donor character of many solvents was seen to cause dissociation of associated metal alkyls and to change the geometry of the metal alkyl monomer. There are various kinds of evidence suggesting that donor solvents or Lewis bases, in general, can change the strength of carbon-metal bonds. In fact, Wittig has proposed a most appealing qualitative interpretation of medium effects on organometallic reactions.[10] Given in terms of complexes, complexes of $R_m M$ with Lewis bases ($B = R_2'O$, $R_3'N$, $X^{\ominus}$, $R'^{\ominus}$, etc.) are termed *ate* complexes and the resulting carbon-metal bonds in $R_m M : B$ are held to be weaker than in uncomplexed $R_m M$. Hence, the R groups are more anionically mobile and the complex is chemically more reactive. The greater

[29] M. S. Kharasch, O. Reinmuth, and F. R. Mayo, *J. Chem. Educ.*, **13**, 7 (1936).
[30] R. E. Dessy et al., *J. Am. Chem. Soc.*, **81**, 2683 (1959); **82**, 686, 689 (1960).
[31] F. R. Jensen and R. J. Ouellette, *J. Am. Chem. Soc.*, **83**, 4477 (1961).

reactivity of organolithium compounds in ethers or amines, compared with solutions in hydrocarbons, is a case in point. On the other hand, complexes of $R_m M$ with Lewis acids $(A = R_3'B, R_3'Al, R_2'Zn)$ are termed *onium* complexes and the resulting carbon bonds in $M[R_3'BR]_n$ are less reactive than in $R_m M$. The air and moisture stability of $Na[B(C_6H_5)_4]$ and the stability of

TABLE 4–4

Bond Parameters of Organometallic Systems[a]

Bond	Length (Å)	Compound	C—M—C Angle (degrees)
Be—C	1.93	$[(CH_3)_2Be]_x$	114° (Be—C—Be, 66°)
Hg—C	2.23	$(CH_3)_2Hg$	180°
B—C	1.56	$(CH_3)_3B$	120°
Al—C	2.01	$[(CH_3)_3Al]_2$	110° (for bridge)
			70° (for Al—C—Al)
In—C	2.16	$[(CH_3)_3In]_4$	—
Si—C	1.88	$(CH_3)_4Si$	tetrahedral
Ge—C	1.98	$(CH_3)_4Ge$	tetrahedral
Sn—C	2.18	$(CH_3)_4Sn$	tetrahedral
Pb—C	2.29	$(CH_3)_4Pb$	tetrahedral
As—C	1.98	$(CH_3)_3As$	96°
Sb—C	2.20	$(CF_3)_3Sb$	100°
Bi—C	2.30	$(C_6H_5)_3Bi$	—
Cr—C	1.92	$Cr(CO)_6$	—
Fe—C	1.84	$Fe(CO)_5$	—
Co—C	1.83	$Co(CO)_4H$	—
Ni—C	1.82	$Ni(CO)_4$	—
Mo—C	2.08	$Mo(CO)_6$	—
W—C	2.06	$W(CO)_6$	—

[a] A. F. Wells, *Structural Inorganic Chemistry*, 3rd ed., Clarendon, Oxford, 1962.

alkali metal alkyls in diethylzinc solution illustrates this situation. The four-center transition state (I) can be seen to involve assisted carbon-metal bond cleavage by synchronous *ate-onium* complexation.[9]

This broad picture of solvent effect is useful, but by no means unerring. It represents accurately the behavior of many organometallics whose reaction pathways involve much nucleophilic initiative by carbanions or pseudo-carbanions. This view fails utterly when the organometallic is functioning as an electrophile. For example, although *n*-butyllithium (carbanionic) adds to 1,1-diphenylethylene more rapidly in ether than in benzene,[32] the presence of

[32] K. Ziegler, F. Crössmann, H. Kleiner, and O. Schäfer, *Ann.*, **473**, 1 (1929).

ethers retards the addition of triphenylaluminum (electrophilic) to alkynes.[33] Hence, a clear understanding of the particular reaction mechanism is necessary to rationalize solvents effects.

Bond Parameters

Even if the amount of σ- and π-character and the over-all polarity of covalent carbon-metal bonds are determined in a precise manner, the physical parameters of bond length and bond strength will continue to be of primary

TABLE 4–5

Bond Energies of Some Carbon–Metal Linkages[a]

Bond	Energy (kcal/mole)	Compound
Zn—C	40	$(CH_3)_2Zn$
Cd—C	32	$(CH_3)_2Cd$
Hg—C	27	$(CH_3)_2Hg$
B—C	89	$(CH_3)_3B$
Si—C	75	$(CH_3)_4Si$
Sn—C	54	$(C_2H_5)_4Sn$
As—C	48	$(CH_3)_3As$
Sb—C	47	$(CH_3)_3Sb$
Bi—C	31	$(CH_3)_3Bi$
Se—C	58	$(C_2H_5)_2Se$

[a] T. L. Cottrell, *The Strength of Chemical Bonds*, 2nd ed., Academic, New York, 1958.

importance. It can be appreciated that bond lengths and bond angles of associated alkyls will be a complex function of structural and medium effects. For unassociated alkyls typical trends in bond lengths can be anticipated. Useful structural data for certain metal alkyls are gathered in Table 4–4 for reference.[34] From the previous discussion of bond polarity, it can be concluded for main group metals that bond length and bond polarity are roughly inversely related. That is to say, the C—M bond lengthens as one goes down in a family or as one goes from right to left in a given period of the periodic table. The interpretation of shortening in C—M over that expected from covalent radii summation in terms of p_π—p_π or d_π—p_π bonding is open to

[33] J. J. Eisch and C. K. Hordis, unpublished studies, 1966.
[34] A. F. Wells, *Structural Inorganic Chemistry*, 3rd ed., Clarendon, Oxford, 1962.

question. One could equally argue that bond polarity is altered when the carbon hybridization is varied.

The strength of a covalent bond generally increases as the bond length decreases. Such estimation of bond strength can be made in terms of bond energies. These bond energies measure the average energy (kcal/mole) necessary to effect homolysis of the carbon-metal bonds to yield two free radicals (R· and ·M in their ground state). Hence, these values may serve as a guide in discussing homolytic reaction pathways, such as the thermolysis of C—M bonds. Representative bond energies are presented in Table 4-5.[35] The thermal stability of boron and silicon alkyls, and the thermal lability of alkyls of the fourth and fifth periods, are reflected in these values.

[35] T. L. Cottrell, *The Strength of Chemical Bonds*, 2nd ed., Academic, New York, 1958.

FIVE

General Chemical
Behavior of
Carbon-Metal Bonds

The carbon-metal bond participates in a wide variety of addition and substitution reactions. The establishment of metal bonds to more electronegative elements or to carbon in a more anionically stable environment seems to be the driving force for most of these transformations:

a. Addition:

$$R—M + Z \rightarrow R—Z—M \qquad (Z = O, S, R_m'M)$$

$$R—M + \underset{}{\overset{}{C}}{=}Z' \rightarrow R—\overset{|}{\underset{|}{C}}—Z'—M \qquad (Z' = C, O, S, N, etc.)$$

b. Substitution:

$$R—M + R'—Z—H \rightarrow R—H + M—Z—R' \qquad \text{metal-hydrogen exchange}$$

$$R—M + R'—X \rightarrow R—X + R'—M \qquad \text{metal-halogen exchange}$$

$$R—M + M'—Y \rightarrow R'—M' + M—Y \quad \text{metal-metal exchange} \qquad (Y = Br, Cl, I, or M')$$

To characterize the scope and limitations of both inorganic and organic reagents reacting with the carbon-metal bond, a survey of basic organometallic reactions will be presented. Their applicability to organometallic synthesis will be treated in Chapter Seven.

Characteristic Reactions

INORGANIC REAGENTS

Halogens and Pseudohalogens. The vigorous attack of fluorine and chlorine on organic compounds themselves makes the presence of a carbon-metal bond unnecessary for reaction. However, molecular bromine and iodine selectively cleave most carbon-metal and carbon-metalloid bonds. The preferential cleavage of phenyl groups from cyclohexyltriphenyllead[1] and the preparation of 4-iododibenzothiophene via a metalation route[2] illustrate the synthetic utility of this method:

$$(C_6H_{11})(C_6H_5)_3Pb + Br_2 \xrightarrow{C_5H_5N} (C_6H_{11})(C_6H_5)_2PbBr + C_6H_5Br \qquad (5\text{-}1)$$

$$(5\text{-}2)$$

The structure of the resulting halo compound serves to prove the position of the previous carbon-metal bond.

With unsymmetrical pseudohalogens, such as nitrosyl chloride, cyanogen halides, nitrogen trihalides, and chloramines, cleavages in both senses have been observed[3]:

$$(5\text{-}3)$$

Oxygen and Sulfur. With the notable exception of mercury alkyls, all the metal alkyls of Groups I–III suffer air oxidation of their carbon-metal bonds. If the metal alkyl is sufficiently volatile, exposure to air can cause spontaneous burning. Under more controlled conditions, such oxidations have been shown to involve hydroperoxides as intermediates[4]:

$$R\text{—}M + O_2 \longrightarrow R\text{—}O\text{—}O\text{—}M \xrightarrow{R\text{—}M} 2R\text{—}O\text{—}M \xrightarrow{H_2O} R\text{—}OH \qquad (5\text{-}4)$$

[1] E. Krause and O. Schlottig, *Ber.*, **58**, 427 (1925).
[2] H. Gilman and J. F. Nobis, *J. Am. Chem. Soc.*, **67**, 1479 (1945).
[3] V. Grignard, E. Bellet, and C. H. Courtot, *Ann. Chim.* (*Paris*), **4** (9), 28 (1915).
[4] (a) A. G. Davies, *Organic Peroxides*, Butterworth, London, 1961, pp. 120–126, 155–160; (b) H. Hock, H. Kropf, and F. Ernst, *Angew. Chem.*, **71**, 541 (1959); (c) C. Walling and S. A. Buckler, *J. Am. Chem. Soc.*, **75**, 4372 (1953); **77**, 6032 (1955).

Although the oxidation of metal alkyls and subsequent hydrolysis can provide good yields of alcohols, metal aryls, on the other hand, tend to give large quantities of hydrocarbon coupling products.[5] Suitable modifications, such as cooxidizing a mixture of the metal aryl and a metal alkyl, or the use of certain higher ethers (anisole or phenetole), can enhance the yield of phenol. The method often has preparative value for alcohols and phenols that might be difficult to prepare by other routes[6]:

$$C_6H_5Li \xrightarrow{O_2} C_6H_5-C_6H_5 \ (65\%) + C_6H_5OH \ (18\%) \qquad (5-5)^{6a}$$

$$\qquad\qquad\qquad 52\% \qquad (5-6)^{6b}$$

Sulfur, or indeed selenium and tellurium, can give rise to products analogous to alcohols and ethers. With these nonmetals the analogous peroxide-like products, R—E—E—R, are readily isolable.

Hydrogen. Since molecular hydrogen can be considered as a "degenerate" alkane (C_nH_{2n+2}, where $n = 0$), its reaction with organometallic compounds can be viewed formally as a proton transfer. If the metal hydride is unstable under the conditions of hydrogenolysis, reduction to the metal ensues:

$$2R-M + 2H_2 \ \rightarrow 2R-H + 2M-H \rightarrow 2RH + 2M + H_2 \qquad (5-7)$$

Derivatives of polyvalent metals can often be treated so as to yield alkylmetal hydrides, as exemplified by the behavior of triethylaluminum[7]:

$$(C_2H_5)_3Al + H_2 \xrightarrow[100° \ atm.]{150°} (C_2H_5)_2AlH + C_2H_6 \qquad (5-8)$$

The ease of such hydrogen cleavages can vary from the room-temperature reaction of alkali metal aryls[8] to the high-temperature (150–300°) and high-pressure cleavage of boron alkyls[9]:

$$C_6H_5K + H_2 \xrightarrow{20°} C_6H_6 + KH \qquad (5-9)$$

$$(C_2H_5)_3B + 3H_2 + N(C_2H_5)_3 \xrightarrow{200-220°} (C_2H_5)_3N:BH_3 + 3C_2H_6 \qquad (5-10)$$

[5] (a) H. Gilman and A. Wood, *J. Am. Chem. Soc.*, **48**, 806 (1926); (b) H. Gilman and K. E. Marple, *Rec. trav. chim.*, **55**, 133 (1936).

[6] (a) E. Müller and T. Töpel, *Ber.*, **72B**, 273 (1939); (b) H. Gilman, L. C. Cheney, and H. B. Willis, *J. Am. Chem. Soc.*, **61**, 951 (1939).

[7] K. Ziegler, H. G. Gellert, H. Lehmkuhl, W. Pfohl, and K. Zosel, *Ann.*, **629**, 13 (1960).

[8] H. Gilman, A. L. Jacoby, and H. Ludeman, *J. Am. Chem. Soc.*, **60**, 2336 (1938).

[9] R. Köster, *Angew. Chem.*, **69**, 94 (1957).

Metals. The ability of active metals to displace less active metals from organometallic compounds, previously cited in the section on metal-organic substrate interactions, seems closely related to the electromotive redox behavior of the metals. The reaction has great preparative utility for the synthesis of solvate-free, active metal alkyls of Groups IA–IIIA. The syntheses of triphenylaluminum[10] and of ethyllithium[11] typify this kind of reaction:

$$3(C_6H_5)_2Hg + 2Al \xrightarrow[\text{xylene}]{140°} 2(C_6H_5)_3Al + 3Hg \qquad (5\text{–}11)$$

$$(C_2H_5)_2Hg + 2Li \longrightarrow 2C_2H_5Li + Hg \qquad (5\text{–}12)$$

Brønsted Acids. Inorganic compounds containing hydrogen bonded to atoms of high electronegativity (X, O, S, N) can cleave carbon-metal bonds very readily. The facile hydrolysis of the alkali and alkaline earth metal alkyls is an occasion for elaborate experimental precaution in handling these compounds:

$$CH_3CH_2^-Na^+ + H\text{—}O\text{—}H \rightarrow CH_3CH_3 + Na^+OH^- + \varDelta \qquad (5\text{–}13)$$

Since the volatile alkane can be monitored volumetrically and the aqueous solution obtained can be analyzed for base or metal cation titrimetrically, the decomposition by Brønsted acids is an important analytical procedure. For carbon-metal bonds more resistant to hydrolysis, acids may be necessary. Thus, although aluminum alkyls suffer rupture of all three bonds in R_3Al upon hydrolysis, gallium, indium, and thallium alkyls undergo cleavage of only one bond under mild hydrolysis, while boron alkyls are inert. Carboxylic or mineral acids, however, cleave all C—M bonds in Group III alkyls, as well as C—M bonds in almost all situations. It is worthy of note that such bonds in Group IVA organometalloids can be hydrolyzed more readily by basic reagents than by acidic reagents.

By substitution of deuterium oxide for water, specifically deuterium-labeled hydrocarbons can be synthesized. This technique permits the preparation of important organic compounds for n.m.r. spectroscopic studies.[12] But the chief significance of deuterolysis is that identification of the resulting deuterated hydrocarbon establishes the position of the previous carbon-metal bond[13]:

[10] H. Gilman and K. E. Marple, *Rec. trav. chim.*, **55**, 135 (1936).
[11] W. Schlenk and J. Holtz, *Ber.*, **50**, 262 (1917).
[12] G. Wilke and H. Müller, *Ann.*, **618**, 267 (1958).
[13] J. J. Eisch and W. C. Kaska, *J. Am. Chem. Soc.*, **85**, 2165 (1963).

$$C_6H_5-C{\equiv}C-CH_3 + R_2AlH \longrightarrow \underset{\underset{R_2Al\ \ H}{|\quad\ |}}{C_6H_5-C{=}C-CH_3} + \underset{\underset{H\ \ AlR_2}{|\quad\ |}}{C_6H_5-C{=}C-CH_3}$$

(5-14)

$$\underset{\underset{D\ \ H}{|\quad|}}{C_6H_5-C{=}C-CH_3} \qquad \underset{\underset{H\ \ D}{|\quad|}}{C_6H_5-C{=}C-CH_3}$$

80% (by n.m.r.) 20%

Naturally with allylic organometallics it is possible that hydrolysis may occur with partial rearrangement. In such cases it is hazardous to conclude anything about the original positions of the carbon-metal bonds merely from the hydrocarbons formed. Physical measurements performed on the organo-metallic are necessary in structure assignments (*vide infra*). In the preceding case, only a physical method analysis (n.m.r.) of the original aluminum system could lend real assurance on the course of hydrolysis.

Lewis Salt Formation. The polar character of the carbon-metal bond, on the one hand, and the available orbitals on the metal atom, on the other hand, allow the interaction of organometallic compounds with either inorganic Lewis acids or Lewis bases (it seems appropriate to include here organic derivatives of such Lewis acids or bases). The nature of the Lewis base can range from that of an anion (halide, cyanide, alkoxide, amide, carbanion):

$$2(CH_3CH_2)_3Al \xrightarrow{KF} [(CH_3CH_2)_3Al]_2KF \xrightarrow{KF} 2K[Al(CH_2CH_3)_3F] \quad (5\text{-}15)^{[14]}$$

$$C_6H_5-Li + C_6H_5^-Na^+ \rightarrow Na^+[Li(C_6H_5)_2] \qquad (5\text{-}16)^{[15]}$$

to alkyl derivatives of ammonia, water, hydrogen sulfide, and phosphines:

$$(C_6H_5)_3Al + (CH_3CH_2)_2\ddot{O}: \rightarrow (C_6H_5)_3\bar{Al} \leftarrow \overset{|}{O}(CH_2CH_3)_2 \qquad (5\text{-}17)^{[16]}$$

$$[(C_6H_5)_3P]_2NiBr_2 + C_6H_5MgBr \rightarrow [(C_6H_5)_3P]_2Ni(C_6H_5)_2 \qquad (5\text{-}18)^{[17]}$$

Lewis acids, conversely, tend to coordinate with the anionic moiety (or incipient anion) of an organometallic compound.[18] Depending upon the nature of the Lewis acid, this may occur as a prelude to an alkyl exchange reaction[19]:

$$(C_6H_5)_3C-Li + B(C_6H_5)_3 \rightleftharpoons Li^+[B(C_6H_5)_3(C_6H_5)_3C]^- \qquad (5\text{-}19)^{[18]}$$

[14] K. Ziegler, R. Köster, H. Lehmkuhl, and K. Reinert, *Ann.*, **629**, 33 (1960).
[15] G. Wittig and E. Benz, *Ber.*, **91**, 873 (1958).
[16] G. Wittig and D. Wittenberg, *Ann.*, **606**, 13 (1957).
[17] J. Chatt and B. L. Shaw, *J. Chem. Soc.*, **1960**, 1718.
[18] G. Wittig and P. Raff, *Ann.*, **573**, 195 (1952).
[19] R. Köster, *Ann.*, **618**, 31 (1958).

$$(CH_3CH_2)_3Al + BF_3 \longrightarrow [(CH_3CH_2)_2Al \overset{\overset{\displaystyle F}{\diagdown}}{\underset{\underset{\displaystyle CH_3}{|}}{CH_2}} BF_2] \longrightarrow \begin{matrix} (CH_3CH_2)_3B \\ + \\ AlF_3 \end{matrix}$$

$$(5\text{-}20)^{19}$$

The interplay of such potential equilibria is of prime importance in determining metal alkyl association and solvation phenomena and hence the reactivity of such organometallic systems.

Metal Salts. If the metal salts of metals ($M'Z_m$) having a greater oxidation potential are treated with the metal alkyl (R_mM) of a less reactive metal, at most anion complexation will occur:

$$(CH_3CH_2)_3Ga + K^+F^- \rightarrow K[Ga(CH_2CH_3)_3F] \qquad (5\text{-}21)^{20}$$

However, if M' is less active than M, alkyl transfer can ensue:

$$2CH_3MgI + HgBr_2 \rightarrow (CH_3)_2Hg + 2MgBrI \qquad (5\text{-}22)^{21}$$

$$CH_3CH_2Li + (CH_3CH_2)_2TlCl \rightarrow (CH_3CH_2)_3Tl + LiCl \qquad (5\text{-}23)^{22}$$

Finally, with metals or metalloids of similar oxidation potential, equilibria can be established:

$$(C_6H_5)_4Pb + AlCl_3 \rightleftharpoons (C_6H_5)_3PbCl + C_6H_5AlCl_2 \qquad (5\text{-}24)^{23}$$

ORGANIC REAGENTS

Although a wide variety of organic compounds undergoes reactions with organometallic systems, two main types of transformations may be discerned: exchange of singly bonded groups with R—M; and the addition of R—M to unsaturated organic systems.

Exchanges—Metal-Hydrogen Exchange or Metalation.[24]   In this type an organic pseudo- or Brønsted acid containing an active C—H bond undergoes reaction to form a new carbon-metal bond:

$$R\text{—}H + R'\text{—}M \rightarrow R'\text{—}H + R\text{—}M$$

[20] J. J. Eisch, *J. Am. Chem. Soc.*, **84**, 3605 (1962).
[21] E. Krause, *Ber.*, **54**, 934 (1926).
[22] H. P. A. Groll, *J. Am. Chem. Soc.*, **52**, 2998 (1930).
[23] H. Gilman and L. D. Apperson, *J. Org. Chem.*, **4**, 162 (1939).
[24] H. Gilman and J. W. Morton, Jr., in *Organic Reactions*, Vol. VIII (R. Adams, ed.), Wiley, New York, 1954, p. 258.

The driving force appears to be anionic stability, which may be achieved by establishing the new carbanion on a carbon atom stabilized by inductive or resonance effects. The metalations of phenylacetylene and of anisole by *n*-butyllithium bring out the favorable inductive effect:

$$C_6H_5-C\equiv C-H + C_2H_5Li \rightarrow C_6H_5-C\equiv C-Li + C_2H_6 \qquad (5\text{-}25)[25]$$

$$(5\text{-}26)[26]$$

The facility with which the α-hydrogens of phenylmethanes and their analogs are substituted reflects the importance of anionic delocalization:

$$(C_6H_5)_2CH_2 + n\text{-}C_4H_9Li \longrightarrow \qquad\qquad + n\text{-}C_4H_{10}$$

$$(5\text{-}27)[26]$$

$$+ C_6H_5Li \longrightarrow \qquad\qquad + C_6H_6 \qquad (5\text{-}28)[27]$$

$$CH_2{=}CHCH_3 + CH_3CH_2{}^-Na^+ \longrightarrow CH_2{=}CH{-}CH_2Na^+ + CH_3CH_3$$

$$(5\text{-}29)[28]$$

Metal-Halogen Exchange.[29] The "positive" halogen character of certain organic halides is illustrated by their ability to undergo displacement by metal centers:

$$+ n\text{-}C_4H_9Li \longrightarrow \qquad\qquad + n\text{-}C_4H_9Br \qquad (5\text{-}30)[31]$$

$$+ C_6H_5Li \longrightarrow \qquad\qquad + C_6H_5I \qquad (5\text{-}31)[30]$$

[25] T. V. Talalaeva and K. A. Kocheshkov, *Dokl. Akad. Nauk SSSR*, **77**, 621 (1951); through *C.A.*, **45**, 1019 (1951).

[26] H. Gilman and R. L. Bebb, *J. Am. Chem. Soc.*, **61**, 109 (1939).

[27] L. A. Walters, W. H. Hunt, and R. J. Fosbinder, *J. Am. Chem. Soc.*, **63**, 2771 (1941).

[28] A. A. Morton and M. E. T. Holden, *J. Am. Chem. Soc.*, **69**, 1675 (1947).

[29] R. G. Jones and H. Gilman, in *Organic Reactions*, Vol. VI (R. Adams, ed.), Wiley, New York, 1951, pp. 339–366.

[30] H. Gilman, W. Langham, and A. L. Jacoby, *J. Am. Chem. Soc.*, **61**, 106 (1939).

[31] E. Campaigne and W. O. Faye, *J. Am. Chem. Soc.*, **70**, 3941 (1948).

The ease of exchange seems to be the inverse of the halogen's electronegativity. Furthermore, the equilibrium exchange tends to lie in favor of the halogen being bonded to the less electronegative organic group.

Metal-Metal Exchange.[32] By this term is meant the metathesis between two different organometallic compounds, in which the alkyl groups are exchanged. This reaction should be distinguished from metal-metal displacements, in which a more active metal displaces a less active metal from an organometallic compound. In the metathetical exchange the more electropositive metal tends to become associated with the more electronegative

$$n\text{R}_m\text{---M} + m\text{R}_n'\text{---M}' \rightleftharpoons n\text{R}_m'\text{---M} + m\text{R}_n\text{---M}'$$

organic group (cf. Tables 4–1 and 4–2 for the pertinent trends in the metals and the organic moieties, respectively). Some recent examples include lithium-tin and boron-aluminum systems:

$$(\text{C}_6\text{H}_5)_3\text{Sn---CH}{=}\text{CH}_2 + \text{C}_6\text{H}_5\text{Li} \rightarrow (\text{C}_6\text{H}_5)_4\text{Sn} + \text{CH}_2{=}\text{CH---Li} \qquad (5\text{--}32)^{33}$$

$$(\text{C}_6\text{H}_5\text{CH}_2)_3\text{B} + (\text{CH}_3\text{CH}_2)_3\text{Al} \rightleftharpoons (\text{CH}_3\text{CH}_2)_3\text{B} + (\text{C}_6\text{H}_5\text{CH}_2)_3\text{Al} \qquad (5\text{--}33)^{34}$$

As might be anticipated, the reaction can attain equilibrium short of completion, when the metals and organic groups are similar in electronic character. Moreover, the rate of such metal-metal exchanges can be astonishingly rapid; thus, the admixing of triethylaluminum and tri-*n*-butylborane at room temperature and the immediate solvolysis of the system at low temperatures (where $\text{R}'\text{R}_2\text{B}$ is inert to H_2O) gave an equimolar mixture of ethane and *n*-butane[34]:

$$(\text{CH}_3\text{CH}_2)_3\text{Al} + (\text{CH}_3\text{CH}_2\text{CH}_2\text{CH}_2)_3\text{B} \rightleftharpoons (\text{CH}_3\text{CH}_2)_n(\text{CH}_3\text{CH}_2\text{CH}_2\text{CH}_2)_{3-n}\text{Al}$$
$$+ \qquad (5\text{--}34)$$
$$(\text{CH}_3\text{CH}_2\text{CH}_2\text{CH}_2)_n(\text{CH}_3\text{CH}_2)_{3-n}\text{B}$$

Metal-Alkyl Exchange. This alkylation of organometallic compounds with alkyl halides and alkyl esters of inorganic acids is an important method of lengthening the carbon skeleton. Since organometallic compounds often are prepared from alkyl halides and the desired metal, metal-alkyl exchange may lead to a coupling side reaction in such procedures:

$$\text{R---X} \xrightarrow{\text{M}} \text{R---M---X} \xrightarrow{\text{RX}} \text{R---R} + \text{MX}_2$$

---

[32] (a) R. G. Jones and H. Gilman, *Chem. Rev.*, **54**, 863 (1954); (b) D. Seyferth and M. A. Weiner, *J. Am. Chem. Soc.*, **84**, 361 (1962); (c) The rates of metal-metal exchanges have been the subject of several investigations: R. E. Dessy et al., *J. Am. Chem. Soc.*, **85**, 1191 (1963), have reported on Mg—Zn, Mg—Cd, Hg—Zn and Hg—Cd; O. A. Reutov, *Rec. Chem. Progr.*, **22**, 1 (1961), observed Hg—Hg^{203} exchanges, and C. R. McCoy and A. L. Allred, *J. Am. Chem. Soc.*, **84**, 912 (1962), observed Zn—Cd exchanges, in addition to some duplication with Dessy's work.

[33] D. Seyferth and M. A. Weiner, *J. Am. Chem. Soc.*, **83**, 3583 (1961).

[34] R. Köster and G. Bruno, *Ann.*, **629**, 102 (1960).

The coupling of simple alkyl and aryl halides by active metals is known to be especially responsive to special pathways involving transition metal catalysis and arene intermediates.[35a] In the other cases of interest, however, simple metal-alkyl exchange seems to occur only with the more reactive alkyl halides and the organoid halides:

$$C_6H_5MgBr + CH_2\!=\!CH\!-\!CH_2\!-\!Br \longrightarrow C_6H_5\!-\!CH_2\!-\!CH\!=\!CH_2 + MgBr_2$$

(5–35)[35b]

(5–36)[36]

$$C_6H_5(CH_2)_2Li + (C_6H_5)_3Si\!-\!Cl \longrightarrow C_6H_5(CH_2)_2Si(C_6H_5)_3 \qquad (5\text{–}37)^{37}$$

ADDITIONS TO UNSATURATED ORGANIC SYSTEMS—CARBONYL SYSTEMS

The carbonyl group in various organic derivatives responds to the more reactive organometallic compounds. As one moves to the right of the main families in Groups I and II, however, the carbon-metal bond becomes less reactive. Thus, R_3Al can furnish one or possibly two bonds which respond to $C\!=\!O$ linkages, whereas boron, zinc and mercury alkyls are, in general, unreactive:

$$(CH_3CH_2)_3Al + 2CO_2 \longrightarrow (CH_3CH_2\overset{\displaystyle O}{\overset{\|}{C}}\!-\!O)_2(CH_3CH_2)Al \qquad (5\text{–}38)^{38}$$

(5–39)[39]

(5–40)[40]

$$+ CdCl_2$$

[35] (a) Cf. V. D. Parker, L. H. Piette, R. M. Salinger, and C. R. Noller, *J. Am. Chem. Soc.*, **86**, 1110 (1964), and V. D. Parker and C. R. Noller, *J. Am. Chem. Soc.*, **86**, 112 (1964), for the cuprous bromide-catalyzed coupling of Grignard reagents with alkyl halides; (b) H. Levy and A. C. Cope, *J. Am. Chem. Soc.*, **66**, 1684 (1944).

[36] H. Gilman, C. G. Brannen, and R. K. Ingham, *J. Org. Chem.*, **22**, 685 (1957).

[37] H. Gilman, A. G. Brook, and L. S. Miller, *J. Am. Chem. Soc.*, **75**, 3757 (1953).

[38] K. Ziegler, F. Krupp, K. Weyer, and W. Larbig, *Ann.*, **629**, 251 (1960).

[39] D. A. Shirley and M. J. Danzig, *J. Am. Chem. Soc.*, **74**, 2935 (1952), prepared 2-thianaphthaldehyde in 62% yield by this route.

[40] (a) J. Cason, *J. Am. Chem. Soc.*, **68**, 2078 (1946); (b) D. A. Shirley, *Organic Reactions*, Vol. VIII (R. Adams, ed.), Wiley, New York, 1954, pp. 28–58; (c) J. Kollonitsch, *Nature*, **188**, 140 (1960), reports that this reaction requires the catalytic action of anhydrous magnesium or lithium halides.

In suitably substituted α,β-unsaturated carbonyl compounds the organo-metallic reagent can add in a Michael fashion:

$$(5\text{--}41)^{41}$$

$$(5\text{--}42)^{42}$$

Azomethine and Nitrile Linkages. The behavior of these functional groups parallels that of carbonyl systems, in that both normal 1,2- and conjugate (1,4- or Michael) additions of organometallic compounds have been observed:

$$(5\text{--}43)^{43}$$

$$(5\text{--}44)^{44}$$

$$(5\text{--}45)^{45}$$

$$(5\text{--}46)^{46}$$

[41] H. Gilman and R. H. Kirby, *J. Am. Chem. Soc.*, **63**, 2046 (1941).
[42] W. A. Mosher and M. L. Huber, *J. Am. Chem. Soc.*, **75**, 4604 (1953).
[43] K. Ziegler and H. Zeiser, *Ann.*, **485**, 174 (1931).
[44] H. Gilman and J. J. Eisch, *J. Am. Chem. Soc.*, **79**, 4423 (1957).
[45] H. Gilman and R. H. Kirby, *J. Am. Chem. Soc.*, **55**, 1265 (1933).
[46] H. Gilman, J. E. Kirby, and C. R. Kinney, *J. Am. Chem. Soc.*, **51**, 2252 (1929).

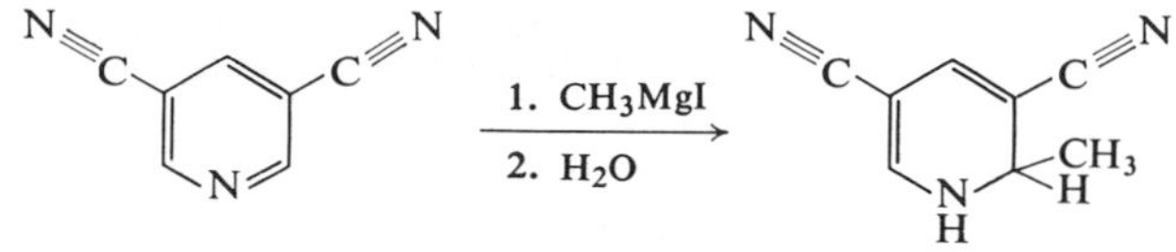

$$\text{(structure)} \xrightarrow[\text{2. } H_2O]{\text{1. } CH_3MgI} \text{(structure)} \qquad (5\text{--}47)^{47}$$

$$C_6H_5\text{—}C\equiv N \xrightarrow{(C_6H_5)_3SiLi} (C_6H_5)_4Si + LiC\equiv N \qquad (5\text{--}48)^{48}$$

The reaction shown in Eq. 5–47 illustrates the relative inertness of the cyano group, with reference to an azomethine system. Moreover, the pseudo-halide character of the nitrile group is revealed in the reaction with triphenylsilyllithium (Eq. 5–48).

Olefins and Acetylenes. The addition of carbon-metal bonds across carbon-carbon unsaturation has been observed with organometallic compounds of Groups IA and IIA and conjugated systems. The aforementioned Michael additions to α,β-unsaturated carbonyl and azomethine systems can be viewed in this light. However, successful additions of such alkyls to unsaturated hydrocarbons have been observed only with highly conjugated linkages or under extreme conditions:

$$\begin{matrix} C_6H_5 \\ \\ C_6H_5 \end{matrix}\!\!\!\!C\!\!=\!\!C\!\!\!\!\begin{matrix} H \\ \\ H \end{matrix} \xrightarrow[\text{2. } H_2O]{\text{1. } n\text{-}C_4H_9Li} (C_6H_5)_2CH\text{—}(CH_2)_4\text{—}CH_3 \qquad (5\text{--}49)^{49}$$

$$H_2C\!\!=\!\!CH_2 \xrightarrow{CH_3CH_2Li} CH_3CH_2\text{—}(CH_2\text{—}CH_2)_n Li \xrightarrow{H_2O} CH_3\text{—}(CH_2)_n CH_3 \quad (5\text{--}50)$$

$$\xrightarrow{\Delta} CH_3CH_2(CH_2)_{n-2}CH\!\!=\!\!CH_2 \qquad (5\text{--}51)^{30a}$$

$$C_5H_5\text{—}C\equiv C\text{—}C_6H_5 \xrightarrow[\text{2. } CO_2; H_3O^+]{\text{1. } C_6H_5Li/Et_2O} \begin{matrix} C_6H_5 \\ \\ C_6H_5 \end{matrix}\!\!\!\!C\!\!=\!\!C\!\!\!\!\begin{matrix} C_6H_5 \\ \\ COOH \end{matrix} \qquad (5\text{--}51a)^{50b}$$

$$\text{(structure —Br, —C}\equiv\text{C—C}_6\text{H}_5) \xrightarrow{n\text{-}C_4H_9Li} \text{(structure —Li, —C}\equiv\text{C—C}_6\text{H}_5) \longrightarrow \text{(structure } C_6H_5, Li)$$

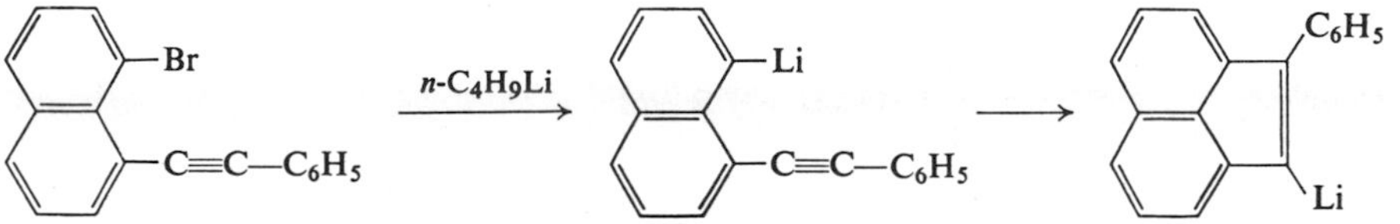

$$(5\text{--}51b)^{50c}$$

The ease of addition increases with Group IIIA alkyls and is especially prominent with aluminum compounds:

[47] R. Lukes and J. Kuthan, *Angew. Chem.*, **72**, 919 (1960).
[48] H. Gilman and D. J. Peterson, *J. Org. Chem.*, **23**, 1895 (1958).
[49] K. Ziegler, F. Crössman, H. Kleiner, and O. Schäfer, *Ann.*, **473**, 1 (1929).
[50] (a) K. Ziegler and H. G. Gellert, *Ann.*, **567**, 195 (1950); (b) J. J. Eisch and W. C. Kaska, *J. Am. Chem. Soc.*, **84**, 1501 (1962); (c) R. E. Dessy and S. A. Kandil, *J. Org. Chem.*, **30**, 3857 (1965).

$$(CH_3CH_2)_3Al \xrightarrow[\Delta/\text{pres.}]{CH_2=CH_2} [CH_3CH_2(CH_2CH_2)_n]_3Al \qquad (5\text{-}52)^{51}$$

$$R-C\equiv C-R \quad
\begin{array}{c}
\xrightarrow{Et_3Al} \quad
\begin{matrix} R-C=C-R \\ | \quad\;\; | \\ Et \;\; AlEt_2 \end{matrix} \\[2em]
\xrightarrow{(C_6H_5)_3Al} \quad
\begin{matrix} R-C=C-R \\ | \quad\;\;\; | \\ C_6H_5 \;\; Al(C_6H_5)_2 \end{matrix}
\end{array}
\qquad (5\text{-}53)^{52}$$

Characterization of Carbon–Metal Bonds

The reactivity of carbon-metal bonds in various molecular environments is one of the principal clues to formulating acceptable organometallic reaction mechanisms. Furthermore, in synthetic applications, a precise monitoring of the formation and destruction of carbon-metal linkages often permits optimal yields of products to be obtained. Finally, in the structure elucidation of new organometallics, the identification of the site of the carbon-metal bond is of prime importance. It is fitting, therefore, to indicate the qualitative and quantitative means available for analyzing organometallic compounds.

QUALITATIVE DETECTION

These methods are based upon the general chemical reactivity of certain carbon-metal bonds to appropriate substrates. A most useful, sensitive color test for organometallics able to add to diaryl ketones is Gilman's Color Test I, shown in Eq. 5-54[53]:

$$(CH_3)_2N-\!\!\left\langle\!\!\bigcirc\!\!\right\rangle\!\!\overset{\overset{\displaystyle O}{\|}}{C}\!\!\left\langle\!\!\bigcirc\!\!\right\rangle\!\!-N(CH_3)_2 + R-M$$

$$\longrightarrow \quad
\begin{matrix} O-M \\ | \\ Ar-C-Ar \\ | \\ R \end{matrix}
\xrightarrow[\text{2. } I_2/\text{HOAc}]{\text{1. } H_3O^+}
\begin{matrix} \quad + \\ Ar-C-Ar \\ | \\ R \end{matrix}
\qquad Ar=p\text{-}(CH_3)_2NC_6H_4 \qquad (5\text{-}54)$$

blue-green color

[51] K. Ziegler, H. G. Gellert, K. Zosel, E. Holzkamp, J. Schneider, M. Söll, and W. R. Kroll, *Ann.*, **629**, 121 (1960).

[52] (a) G. Wilke and H. Müller, *Ann.*, **629**, 222 (1960); (b) J. J. Eisch and W. C. Kaska, *J. Am. Chem. Soc.*, **84**, 1501 (1962); **85**, 2165 (1963); **88**, 2213 (1966).

[53] (a) H. Gilman and F. Schulze, *J. Am. Chem. Soc.*, **47**, 2002 (1925); (b) H. Gilman and L. L. Heck, *ibid.*, **52**, 4949 (1930).

To distinguish between reactive metal *alkyls* and metal *aryls*, the Gilman Color Test II is often useful.[54] Based upon the fact that metal alkyls (Li, Na, etc.), but not metal aryls, will exchange bromine for metal with *p*-bromo-N,N-dimethylaniline, the test thereafter resembles Color Test I[54]:

$$(CH_3)_2N—\underset{}{\bigcirc}—Br + R—M \longrightarrow RBr + (CH_3)_2N—\underset{}{\bigcirc}—M$$

$$\xrightarrow[\substack{1.\ (C_6H_5)CO \\ 2.\ H_3O^+ \\ 3.\ HOAc/I_2}]{} (CH_3)_2N—\underset{}{\bigcirc}—\overset{+}{C}\underset{C_6H_5}{\overset{C_6H_5}{<}} \qquad (5\text{-}55)$$

red color

However, the interaction of organometallic compounds with a gamut of reagents remains the most versatile and reliable method of verifying the presence of carbon-metal bonds in a substance. General points of concern in employing any chemical means of detection are the possible inertness of the carbon-metal bond to be detected towards the reagent used and the possibility of rearrangements occurring during reaction. The former difficulty can be obviated by using a substrate responsive to the type of carbon-metal bond encountered; but the latter point can be especially troublesome with allylic organometallics. The site of the original carbon-metal bond may not be revealed from the derivative isolated[55]:

$$CH_3CH{=}CHCH_2MgX + CH_3\overset{O}{\overset{\|}{C}}{-}\underset{CH_3}{\overset{CH_3}{\bigcirc}}{-}CH_3$$

$$\longrightarrow CH_2{=}CHCH{-}\underset{CH_3\ CH_3}{\overset{OH\ CH_3}{\underset{|\ \ |}{C}}}{-}\underset{CH_3}{\bigcirc}{-}CH_3 \qquad (5\text{-}56)$$

Physical methods of structure determination are indispensable in such cases. Nuclear magnetic resonance spectroscopy is especially valuable in providing data on the ratio of nuclei in different molecular sites. Often a physical measurement can be used in combination with chemical methods to learn whether a given carbon-metal bond cleavage proceeds with rearrangement (allylic or configurational) or not.

---

[54] H. Gilman and J. Swiss, *J. Am. Chem. Soc.*, **62**, 1847 (1940).

[55] (a) J. E. Norlander, W. G. Young, and J. D. Roberts, *J. Am. Chem. Soc.*, **83**, 494 (1961); (b) W. G. Young and J. D. Roberts, *ibid.*, **68**, 1472 (1946).

Labeling reagents for carbon-metal bonds often comprise active hydrogen compounds which can introduce C—D bonds at the site of the original C—M bond. An n.m.r. analysis of the deuterated organic product is a convenient method of structure proof in absence of rearrangements. For reactive organometallics deuterium oxide may be satisfactory; for other alkyls other reagents may be superior (CH_3COOD, ROD, $RC{\equiv}CD$, D_2O with NaOD). In addition, oxidizing agents (O_2, ROOH, H_2O_2 with NaOH), halogen sources (Br_2, I_2, $R{-}C{\equiv}C{-}X$), carbonyl compounds [CO_2, $(C_6H_5)_2C{=}O$] and alkylating agents (R_3SiX, R_3SnX, $C_6H_5CH_2X$, RO_3SAr) may prove advantageous for product isolation (Eqs. 5–57 to 5–59]:

$$(CH_3CH_2CH_2CH_2CH_2)_3B \xrightarrow[-H_2,\,-C_5H_{10}]{\Delta}$$

$$\xrightarrow{H_2O_2/NaOH} \quad CH_3CH(CH_2)_3OH \qquad (5\text{--}57)^{56}$$
$$\underset{OH}{}$$
$$+$$
$$CH_3(CH_2)_4OH$$

$$(5\text{--}58)^{57}$$

$$(5\text{--}59)^{58}$$

If the presence of a carbon-metal linkage in a system has been established by a chemical test, physical measurements can give much insight on the environment of such a linkage. The polarity of this center exerts characteristic influences on the spectral properties of these compounds. For example, the n.m.r. signals of CH_3, CH_2, and CH groups attached to metals occur at relatively high field,[59] the C=C stretch of vinylmetallics is displayed at lower

[56] P. F. Winternitz and A. A. Carrotti, *J. Am. Chem. Soc.*, **82**, 2430 (1960).
[57] J. J. Eisch and W. C. Kaska, *J. Am. Chem. Soc.*, **84**, 1501 (1963).
[58] H. Gilman and R. D. Gorsich, *J. Am. Chem. Soc.*, **77**, 3919 (1955).
[59] E. G. Hoffmann, *Z. Anal. Chem.*, **170**, 177 (1959).

frequencies than in alkenes[60] and the ultraviolet spectra of unsaturated organometallics often display $n - \pi^*$ bands of lower energy.[61] With proper provision for measurement in an inert atmosphere, organometallic reactions can be followed to completion qualitatively by the disappearance of characteristic C=C—M, M—H, or substrate absorptions.

QUANTITATIVE ESTIMATION

The aforementioned physical methods of ultraviolet, infrared, and nuclear magnetic resonance spectroscopy all can be invoked in the quantitative analysis of metal alkyls. It appears that infrared and ultraviolet methods may be inapplicable in many cases where metal alkyl association causes severe deviations from the Beer-Lambert law or where specific solvent effects alter the position or intensity of spectral bands in an unpredictable manner. For sufficiently volatile metal alkyls mass spectrometry and gas-liquid chromatography are gaining in favor, whereas with suitable solvent-adsorbent systems and with the exercise of atmosphere control, there appears no reason why column chromatography could not be applied with success.

Chemical methods for the quantitative analysis of metal alkyls often can be devised for the previously considered derivatizing reactions (CO_2, X_2, or D_2O). Although gravimetric determination of resulting solid derivatives may be undertaken (carboxylic acid yield, for example), a natural, modern supplement is to determine yields by chromatography or by n.m.r. spectroscopy. For example, the position of equilibrium in the halogen-lithium exchange process (Eq. 5–60) has been determined by hydrolysis and gas chromatographic analysis of the alkyl halide ratio[62]:

$$R—Li + R'—X \rightleftharpoons R—X + R'—Li \qquad (5–60)$$

The major pitfalls in chemical estimation are the intrusion of side reactions (thus, the formation of $R_2C{=}O$, R_3COH, and RCO_2H from R—Li and CO_2) or incomplete reaction of all carbon-metal bonds with the reagent.

One general reaction adaptable to the estimation of all readily hydrolyzed metal alkyls is that of hydrolytic decomposition of the organometallic and the titration of the total alkali thereby liberated[63]:

$$R—M + HOH \rightarrow RH + M^+ + OH^- \qquad (5–61)$$

[60] V. F. Moronov, Y. P. Egorov, and A. D. Petrov, *Dokl. Acad. Nauk. SSSR, Otd. Khim. Nauk*, 1400 (1959).

[61] (a) R. Waack and M. A. Doran, *J. Am. Chem. Soc.*, **85**, 1651 (1963); (b) cf. J. J. Eisch, *Organometallic Syntheses*, Vol. 2, Academic, New York, for a compilation of useful spectroscopic data and for practical considerations in obtaining such data.

[62] D. E. Applequist and D. F. O'Brien, *J. Am. Chem. Soc.*, **85**, 743 (1963).

[63] H. Gilman, P. D. Wilkinson, W. P. Fishel, and C. H. Meyers, *J. Am. Chem. Soc.*, **45**, 150 (1923).

For uncontaminated samples this method is quite reliable; however, unfortunately the RM types undergoing hydrolysis readily often suffer facile oxidation as well. As a consequence, oxidation products present (metal alkoxide, ROM) will contribute a deceiving amount of alkali upon hydrolysis. To obviate this, a combination of derivatization and hydrolysis have been employed to obtain a more reliable measure of actual C—M bonds (X = A—B)[64]:

$$\underbrace{R-O-M + R-M}_{} + X-Z \longrightarrow R-O-M + R-Z + M-X \qquad (5\text{-}62)$$

$$\downarrow \begin{array}{l} \text{1. } H_2O \\ \text{2. } H^+ \text{(quant.)} \end{array} \qquad\qquad \downarrow \begin{array}{l} \text{1. } H_2O \\ \text{2. } H^+ \text{(quant.)} \end{array}$$

$$\text{titer A} \qquad\qquad\qquad \text{titer B}$$

Clearly with organic derivatives of metalloids, some method more feasible than a simple neutralization may prove necessary. Titrations involving complex ion formation (F^-, EDTA, etc.) may be carried out on the metal alkyl hydrolysates. In a complementary sense, the hydrocarbons obtained upon hydrolysis may be subjected to vapor-phase chromatographic and/or mass spectrometric analysis. Such data on the total amount and ratios of different hydrocarbons formed can give an estimate of the equivalent weight and metameric nature of the metal alkyl (for example, Eq. 5–63)[65]:

$$CH_3Al(CH_2CH_3)_2 \xrightarrow{H_2O} CH_4 + 2CH_3CH_3 + Al(OH)_3 \qquad (5\text{-}63)$$

Reactivity Traits of Individual Organometallics

In Chapter Four the bonding in organometallic compounds was analyzed into factors stemming from the metal center and from the organic group, respectively. Some generalizations also were made concerning the reactivity of various carbon-metal bonds. In this section the role of the metal M and of the organic group R in R_mM will be considered as to the relative ease with which addition, substitution, rearrangement, and elimination reactions occur. In situations where all four modes of reaction are conceivable with a given organometallic, orders of preference (reactivity rules) are not simple, but also depend upon experimental conditions. The empirically determined reactivity rules for organometallics were determined by Gilman and coworkers[66] principally from studies conducted in ether. Although these rules are most useful in describing the ease with which addition of RM to C=O linkages results, they may be expected to fail to predict relative competition between

[64] H. Gilman and A. H. Haubein, *J. Am. Chem. Soc.*, **66**, 1515 (1944).

[65] K. Ziegler and H. G. Gellert, *Ann.*, **629**, 20 (1960).

[66] H. Gilman in *Organic Chemistry*, 2nd ed., Vol. 1 (H. Gilman, ed.), Wiley, New York, 1943, pp. 520–524.

two processes, such as addition and substitution. Also reactions in solvents other than ether may diverge from the predictions of Gilman's rules. Thus purely on a polarity basis, the union of the most electropositive metal ion, francium, with a localized alkyl anion should be the most reactive organometallic compound. However, the substrate can play a decisive role in reactivity orders. For even though alkali metal alkyls are felt to be more reactive than Group III alkyls, certain reactions are realized only with the latter. In the interaction of RM with alkynes, organoaluminum reagents add more rapidly. In fact, with terminal alkynes alkali metal alkyls cause metalation instead:

$$R-C{\equiv}C-Li^{67} \xleftarrow{R'Li} R-C{\equiv}C-H \xrightarrow{R'_3Al} \underset{R'}{\overset{R}{>}}C{=}C\underset{AlR'_2}{\overset{H}{<}} \quad {}^{68}(5\text{-}64)$$

The striking effect of solvent is seen in the observation that diethyl ether accelerates the metalating action of RLi toward hydrocarbons. On the other hand, $R_3'Al$ in ether (as etherate) does not add to alkynes. Indeed, in tertiary amine media $R_3'Al \cdot NR_3''$ metalates the terminal alkyne.[69] Clearly a detailed mechanism is necessary to rationalize such divergent facts, and some attention will be devoted to this aspect in the next section.

The suitability in chemical reactions of particular metal alkyls deserves comment. As to the metals involved, certain generalizations about feasibility of reactions can be made. First, the most reactive alkyls in substitution processes (metal-hydrogen, metal-metal, metal-halogen, and metal-alkyl exchanges) are those of Groups IA and IIA. For convenience of preparation and versatility, organolithium compounds are possibly the reagents of choice. Grignard reagents suffer from steric hindrance in some cases and do not undergo metal-hydrogen and metal-halogen exchanges with ease. Organosodium and organopotassium reagents cannot be prepared in ether and are often too indiscriminant in their modes of reaction. Second, the alkyls and hydrides of Group IIIA are the most useful reagents for establishing C—C or C—H bonds by adding organometallics to unconjugated olefins and acetylenes. Aluminum alkyls are superior in forming C—C bonds and boron hydrides are the most convenient for preparing boron alkyls by hydroboration. Third, the alkyls of Groups IA and IIA are sufficiently reactive to cleavage reagents for C—M bonds that many derivatives can be made with consumption of all C—M bonds. With Groups IIIA and IVA alkyls the C—M bonds often will be attacked with decreasing ease: $R-MR_2 > R-MRZ > R-MZ_2$. Hence all available C—M bonds may not respond to certain reagents (for example, CO_2, HX).

[67] R. T. Arnold and G. Smolinsky, *J. Am. Chem. Soc.*, **82**, 4918 (1960).
[68] G. Wilke and H. Müller, *Ann.*, **629**, 222 (1960).
[69] P. Binger, *Angew. Chem.*, **75**, 918 (1963).

The nature of the organic group attached to the metal was seen to play a significant part in determining the structure and reactivity of the C—M bond. Of interest here are the reaction characteristics which have been observed with specific groups. The methyl group, for example, leads to highly associated organometallics of Groups IA–IIIA. In general, such methylmetallics have a lower order of reactivity than those of higher alkylmetallics, possibly due to the necessity of monomeric R_mM for normal reactivity. In addition, methyl derivatives cannot undergo facile elimination of metal hydride and hence are relatively thermostable.

Higher primary alkylmetallic types (p-RM) RCH_2CH_2M and R_2CHCH_2M are less associated than their methyl relatives and hence more soluble in organic solvents, lower-melting, and more reactive. The carbon skeleton, however, permits transformations not allowed in the methyl case. For example, thermal rearrangement and/or elimination reactions can occur, depending upon the nature of the substituents. The formation of isobutylene from triisobutylaluminum and the rearrangement of 2,2,2-triphenylethyl-lithium are cases in point:

$$[(CH_3)_2CHCH_2]_3Al \xrightarrow{\Delta} [(CH_3)_2CHCH_2]_2Al—H + (CH_3)_2C{=}CH_2{\uparrow} \quad (5\text{–}65)\,[70]$$

$$(C_6H_5)_3CCH_2Li \longrightarrow (C_6H_5)_2CLiCH_2C_6H_5 \qquad\qquad (5\text{–}66)\,[71]$$

Passing to systems having metals bonded to secondary or tertiary alkyl groups (s-RM and t-RM), one finds an increase in reactivity of the metal alkyl, together with accentuated steric demands for the reagent. (As a result, auto-complexation tendencies are further decreased.) The latter factor may suppress the desired reaction completely and force the system to taken an entirely new course [72]:

$$(CH_3)_2CH—\overset{\overset{\displaystyle O}{\|}}{C}—CH(CH_3)_2 \xrightarrow{CH_3MgBr} (CH_3)_2CH—\underset{\underset{\displaystyle CH_3}{|}}{\overset{\overset{\displaystyle OMgBr}{|}}{C}}—CH(CH_3)_2 \quad (95\%) \quad (5\text{–}67)$$

$$\xrightarrow{t\text{-}C_4H_9MgBr} (CH_3)_2CH—\underset{\underset{\displaystyle H}{|}}{\overset{\overset{\displaystyle OMgBr}{|}}{C}}—CH(CH_3)_2 \quad (65\%) \quad (5\text{–}68)$$

[70] K. Ziegler, H. Martin, and F. Krupp, *Ann.*, **629**, 14 (1960).
[71] (a) E. Grovenstein, Jr., and L. P. Williams, Jr., *J. Am. Chem. Soc.*, **83**, 412 (1961); (b) H. E. Zimmerman and A. Zweig, *ibid.*, **83**, 1196 (1961).
[72] F. C. Whitmore and R. S. George, *J. Am. Chem. Soc.*, **64**, 1239 (1942).

Types such as

$$
\begin{array}{ccc}
& \text{H} & \\
& | & \\
\text{R}-&\text{C}-\text{CH}_3 & \\
& | & \\
& \text{M} &
\end{array}
\quad \text{or} \quad
\begin{array}{cc}
\text{H} & \text{R}' \\
| & | \\
\text{R}-\text{C}-\text{C}-\text{R}'' \\
| & | \\
\text{H} & \text{M}
\end{array}
$$

may undergo thermal isomerization and generate a new alkyl having the metal attached to a more electronegative carbon; X_c increasing in the sequence, t-RM $<$ s-RM $<$ p-RM:

$$
\begin{array}{cc}
\text{CH}_3 & \text{H} \\
| & | \\
[\text{CH}_3-\text{C}-]_3\text{B} \longrightarrow [\text{CH}_3-\text{C}-\text{CH}_2]_3\text{B} \\
| & | \\
\text{CH}_3 & \text{CH}_3
\end{array}
\qquad (5\text{–}69)^{73}
$$

A parallel tendency is the ability of the foregoing types to undergo extremely facile metal hydride elimination. Indeed, this strongly suggests that organometallic rearrangements, such as those in Eq. 5–69, can proceed via addition-elimination pathways. Evidence from diverse chemical reactions (the Wittig rearrangement,[74] "carbanion" rearrangements (Eq. 5–66), and the isomerization of vinylaluminum systems favors such a viewpoint[75]:

$$
\begin{array}{ccc}
\text{Li} & \text{Li}-\text{R} & \text{R} \\
| & \ddot{|} & | \\
\text{C}_6\text{H}_5-\text{C}-\text{O}^{\diagup \text{R}} \longrightarrow [\text{C}_6\text{H}_5-\text{C}-\text{O}] \longrightarrow \text{C}_6\text{H}_5-\text{C}-\text{O}^{\diagup \text{Li}} \\
| & | & | \\
\text{H} & \text{H} & \text{H}
\end{array}
\quad (5\text{–}70)^{74}
$$

$$
\begin{array}{ccccc}
\text{R}\diagdown \quad \diagup \text{R} & & \text{H} & & \text{R}\diagdown \quad \diagup \text{AlR}'_2 \\
\quad \text{C}{=}\text{C} & \xrightarrow{\text{R}'_2\text{AlH}} & \text{R}-\text{C}-\text{C}\diagdown^{\text{AlR}'_2}_{\text{R}} & \xrightarrow{-\text{R}'_2\text{AlH}} & \quad \text{C}{=}\text{C} \\
\text{H}\diagup \quad \diagdown \text{AlR}'_2 & & | \quad \text{AlR}'_2 & & \text{H}\diagup \quad \diagdown \text{R} \\
& & \text{H} & &
\end{array}
$$
$$
(5\text{–}71)^{75}
$$

As discussed in the last chapter, organic groups attached to carbon having unsaturation α,β or β,γ to the carbon-metal bond have a distinctly different reactivity than their alkylmetallic relatives. Here the chief concern is their mode of reaction. Vinyl and aryl organometallics may undergo position or geometrical isomerization of their carbon-metal bond in a number of ways. Vinylmetallics may isomerize (Eq. 5–72) by metal hydride elimination, which

[73] G. F. Hennion, P. A. McCusker, E. C. Ashby, and A. J. Rutkowski, *J. Am. Chem. Soc.*, **79**, 5190 (1957).
[74] P. T. Lansbury and V. A. Pattison, *J. Org. Chem.*, **27**, 1933 (1962).
[75] J. J. Eisch and W. C. Kaska, *J. Am. Chem. Soc.*, **85**, 2165 (1963).

is simply the reverse reaction of their formation from alkynes and metal hydrides[75]:

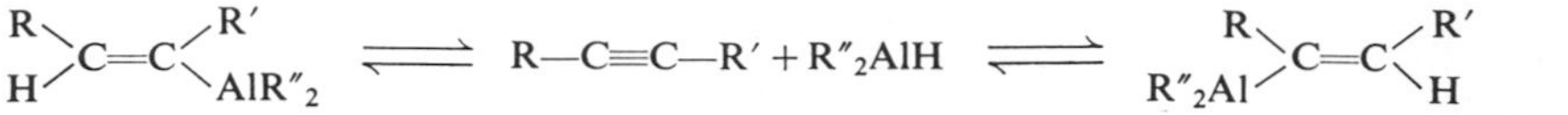

$$(5-72)$$

A related type of metal hydride elimination has been observed with substituted arylmetallics, leading to a novel cyclization[15]:

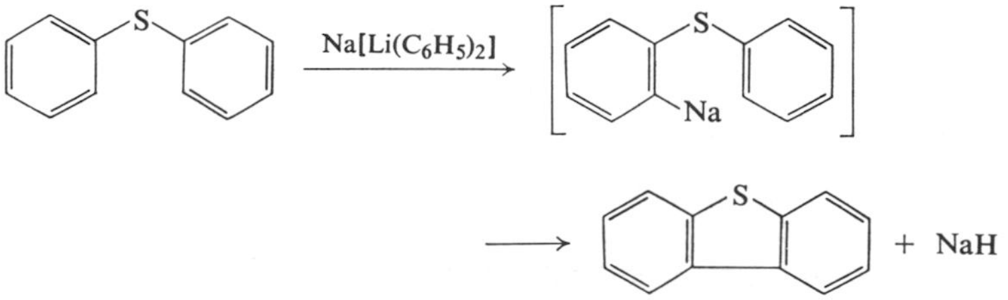

$$+ \text{ NaH} \qquad (5-73)$$

Other modes of isomerization will be treated in Chapter Six.

Vinylmetalloids may be able to react in a unique manner without cleavage of their carbon-metal bond. Of the many olefin reactions which vinylmetallics undergo, the bimolecular coupling with lithium metal is most instructive[76]:

$$(5-74)$$

It is reasonable to ascribe the electron affinity of the formally unconjugated vinyl group to the operation of d_π–p_π delocalization.

With allylic or propargylic metallics the possibility of allylic rearrangements arises. Such rearrangements may occur in the metal alkyl system itself, as with allylmagnesium halides, or in the process of interacting with an organic substrate (Eq. 5–56).

At present, not much is known of the effect of unsaturation located in the γ,δ-position or further removed from the carbon-metal bond. In certain cases carbocyclization has been realized[77] (Eq. 5–75); conversely, strained cycloalkylcarbinyl metallics often suffer thermal ring rupture[78] (Eq. 5–76):

[76] J. J. Eisch and R. J. Beuhler, *J. Org. Chem.*, **28**, 2876 (1963).
[77] J. J. Eisch and G. R. Husk, *J. Org. Chem.*, **31**, 3419 (1966).
[78] P. T. Lansbury, V. A. Pattison, W. A. Clement, and J. D. Sidler, *J. Am. Chem. Soc.*, **86**, 2247 (1964).

$$(5\text{-}75)$$

$$CH_2=CHCH_2CH_2Li \qquad (5\text{-}76)$$

Mechanistic Considerations

TRANSITION-STATE MODELS

The cleavage of covalent carbon-metal bonds of various types can involve homolytic or heterolytic scission. The former process can be fostered by the use of free radical sources, thermolysis or photolysis with a given metal alkyl, or by choosing a weak carbon-metal bond. The smaller bond energies of the alkyls of mercury, thallium, lead, bismuth, and probably most of the transition metals favor homolytic bond rupture. Structural factors favoring such homolysis are both the reorganizational energy of the R radical (for example, allylic delocalization) and the energy separation between the highest occupied and the lowest unoccupied molecular orbital of R_mM (*vide supra*). On the other hand, heterolytic bond cleavage of covalent metal alkyls seems more probable with polar substrates. These reagents include polar systems bearing $C=O$, $C=N$, $H-O$, $H-N$, $H-X$ linkages, as well as homopolar reagents having polarizable linkages, such as $X-X$, $C=C$, and $C\equiv C$. Finally with saline organometallics, having principally electrostatic attraction between the metal ion–carbanion parts, one need only decide which ion initiates a clear polar attack on the substrate. It should be borne in mind that, even with saline organometallics and polar substrates, electron transfer may predominate over group transfer[78a]:

$$
R-R + R'\!-\!\underset{\underset{M^+O^-}{|}}{\overset{\overset{R'}{|}}{C}}\!-\!\underset{\underset{O^-M^+}{|}}{\overset{\overset{R'}{|}}{C}}\!-\!R' \longleftarrow R'\!-\!\underset{\underset{O^\ominus M^\oplus}{|}}{\overset{\overset{\cdot}{C}}}\!-\!R' \xleftarrow{R_2'C=O} R^\ominus M^\oplus \xrightarrow{R_2'C=O} R\!-\!\underset{\underset{R'}{|}}{\overset{\overset{R'}{|}}{C}}\!-\!O^\ominus M^\oplus
$$

The associated and solvated character of Groups IA–IIIA alkyls themselves makes the formation of complexes with substrates a likely possibility. The nature of these complexes and their relation to the reaction mechanism have been the subject of much speculation. In the past, mechanistic discussions of

[78a] G. A. Russell, E. G. Janzen, and E. T. Strom, *J. Am. Chem. Soc.*, **86**, 1807 (1964).

organometallic reactions have emphasized carbanionic attack of the organic group upon the substate. Much of the chemistry of the saline organometallics can be correlated with such a nucleophilic viewpoint (I). With Na, K, Rb, and Cs alkyls structural data suggest an ionic lattice and the metal gegenion may be merely a spectator in the subsequent reaction. At most, it may co-ordinate with some Lewis base center in the substrate (Ia). Since Lewis acidity in metal ions seems to decrease in descending the alkali metal family (Table 2–1), the most pronounced nucleophilic reagents might be the francium alkyls.

On the other hand, it is unreasonable to use the nucleophilic picture with covalent metal alkyls. Not only the lower polarity of the carbon-metal linkage but the increased Lewis acidity of the metal center in R_mM makes a type of electrophilic initiation more appealing (II). *A priori*, this electrophilic attack seems reasonable for the alkyls of Group III. However, with metals of decreasing Lewis acidity and with unsaturated R groups (vinyl, phenyl, and allyl), a combination of electrophilic attack by M and nucleophilic bridging by R may be operative (IIa). In the case of low polarity in substrate and metal alkyl (O_2 and R_3B; R—N=N—R and R'MgX), induced homolysis through a four-center transition state may be attained (III). In the foregoing cases of electrophilic, nucleophilic, and homolytic attack, some type of four-center atom alignment is proposed. But the detailed mechanisms of specific organometallics actually may require the cooperation of two or more R_mM units in the rate-determining step. For example, structure IIIa suggests a chain reaction for certain homolytic processes. Likewise, the Lewis acid in Ia and IIa may be a separate species from that providing the carbanion (IV, V, and VI).

As these transition-state alternatives have different kinetic and stereochemical consequences, a prudent choice demands careful study of product structure and rate laws. In the following discussion some reactions bearing on the question of transition-state models will be considered.

With the fully developed carbanions of sodium and potassium alkyls, nucleophilic attack by the alkyl ion on the positive center seems to be involved:

$$4Na^\oplus \quad CH_3CH_2^\ominus \quad + \quad SnCl_4 \quad \longrightarrow \quad (CH_3CH_2)_4Sn + 4NaCl \qquad (5\text{-}77)$$

Although it is tempting to view this process as an S_N2 attack from the rear side of the Sn—Cl bond, actually a type of flank attack (utilizing tin 5 *d*-orbitals) may occur (VII). Especially with organolithium compounds, the

VII

partial covalence of the C—Li bond appears to favor some synchronous bond-making and bond-breaking process. A four-center, front-side flank attack obviously is involved in the rapid metal-halogen exchange between triptycyl bromide and *n*-butyllithium[79]:

$$(5\text{-}78)$$

The geometry of the triptycene prevents rear-side attack and also is unfavorable for the step-wise generation of the triptycyl anion. Furthermore, in situations where either the developing carbanion of covalent RM or the developing electron deficiency of the substrate have allylic character, one is prompted to postulate six-center transition states (Eqs. 5–79 and 5–80):

[79] G. Wittig, *Tetrahedron*, **3**, 91 (1958).

$$C_6H_5CH=CHCH_2MgX \xrightarrow{R_2C=O} \left[\begin{array}{c} (CH_3)_2C=CH \\ R_2C \diagdown \diagup CH_2 \\ O\cdots Mg \\ | \\ X \end{array} \right] \longrightarrow \begin{array}{c} C_6H_5CH-CH=CH_2 \\ | \\ R_2C \\ | \\ OMgX \end{array} \quad (5\text{-}79)^{80}$$

$$\begin{array}{c} O \\ \| \\ C_6H_5CH=CHCC_6H_5 \end{array} \xrightarrow{(C_6H_5)_3Al} \left[\begin{array}{c} C_6H_5CH=CH \\ \diagup \diagdown \\ C_6H_5 \diagup C-C_6H_5 \\ Al\cdots O \\ | \\ C_6H_5 \ C_6H_5 \end{array} \right] \longrightarrow \begin{array}{c} (C_6H_5)_2CH-CH \\ \diagdown \\ C-C_6H_5 \\ (C_6H_5)_2Al-O \diagup \\ (5\text{-}80)^{81} \end{array}$$

STEREOCHEMISTRY

The stereochemical features of organometallic reactions offer the most penetrating insight into transition-state models. Centers of dissymmetry in the organometallic reagent itself or in the substrate can serve as a probe of the optical isomeric character of the process. Likewise, the behavior of vinyl-metallics in cleavage reaction serves to point up the geometrical isomeric selectivity. Preparing optically active organometallics of Groups IA and IIA is generally a difficult task. By use of the optically active (+)1-bromo-1-methyl-2,2-diphenylcyclopropane, however, an optically active Grignard reagent[82] and an active organolithium compound[83] (with $n\text{-}C_4H_9Li$) have been prepared. Significantly, the lithium reagent can be carbonated with 100% retention of configuration and activity:

$$\begin{array}{ccc} C_6H_5 \quad CH_3 & & C_6H_5 \quad CH_3 \\ C_6H_5 \diagup\!\!\!\triangle\!\!\!\diagdown Li & \xrightarrow[\text{2. H}_3O^+]{\text{1. CO}_2} & C_6H_5 \diagup\!\!\!\triangle\!\!\!\diagdown COOH \end{array} \quad (5\text{-}81)$$

VIII

A flank attack in the formation and carbonation of VIII receives strong support from these observations. However, in the coupling reaction between optically active 2-chlorooctane and ethylsodium, 80% of the 3-methylnonane produced was optically active with inverted configuration and 20% was racemic. This finding supports the operation principally of an S_N2 mechanism. On the other hand, 2-bromooctane coupled with ethylsodium to yield 97% of racemic product.[84a] In a complementary manner, the addition of Grignard

[80] R. H. DeWolfe et al., *J. Am. Chem. Soc.*, **79**, 4798 (1957).

[81] H. Gilman and R. H. Kirby, *J. Am. Chem. Soc.*, **63**, 2046 (1941).

[82] H. M. Walborsky and A. E. Young, *J. Am. Chem. Soc.*, **83**, 2595 (1961).

[83] H. M. Walborsky and F. J. Impastato, *J. Am. Chem. Soc.*, **81**, 5835 (1959).

[84] (a) Cf. E. LeGoff, S. E. Ulrich, and D. B. Denney, *J. Am. Chem. Soc.*, **80**, 622 (1958); (b) D. J. Cram and F. D. Greene, *ibid.*, **75**, 6005 (1953); (c) D. J. Cram, F. A. A. Elhafez, and H. L. Nyquist, *ibid.*, **76**, 22 (1954); (d) D. J. Cram and K. R. Kopecky, *ibid.*, **81**, 2748 (1959).

reagents and organolithium compounds to carbonyl substrates containing adjacent asymmetric centers has been used to probe steric factors in asymmetric induction.[84b, c, d] In the addition of RM to IX, that diastereomer was found to predominate which would be formed most easily from the conformer complex shown in X. If the adjacent asymmetric center bears a coordinating center, then conformer XI will be important. With either X or XI, the carbanionic alkyl group will approach the carbon of the C=O group from the less hindered side:

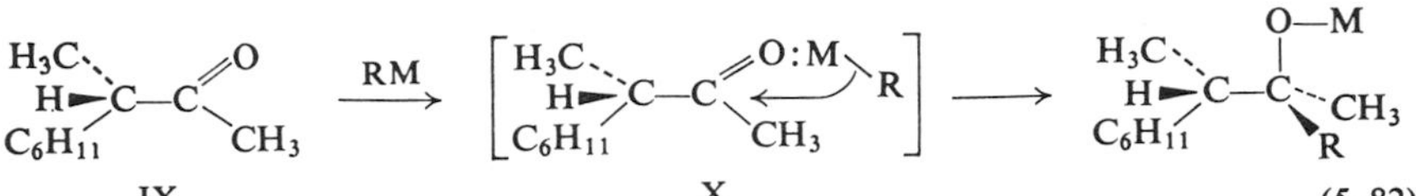

(5–82)

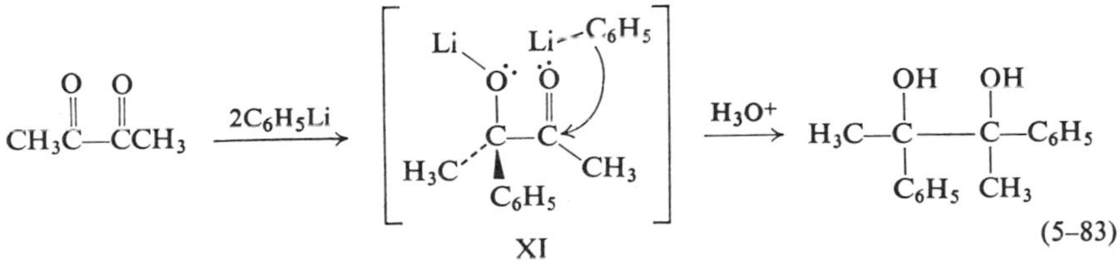

(5–83)

The retention of geometrical configuration is observed in many reactions of vinylmetallics. Only with alkali metal derivatives does isomerization occur with facility. Thus *cis-* and *trans-*propenyllithium prepared from the corresponding bromides and lithium metal in ether are configurationally stable and undergo reaction with retention of configuration[85] (Eq. 5–84, R = CH$_3$, R' = H). In contrast, arylvinyllithiums are stable in hydrocarbon media but isomerize rather readily in ether solution (Eq. 5–84, R, R' = C$_6$H$_5$). The covalent vinylmetallics undergo addition and substitution without configurational change. The preparation of the propenyllithiums by a lithium-tin

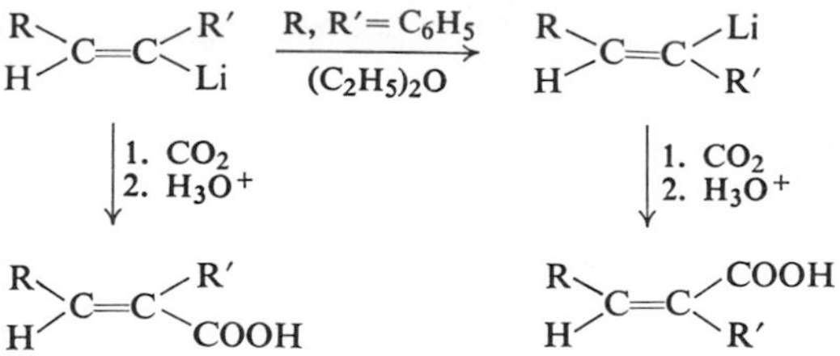

(5–84)

exchange process (Eq. 5–85) and the addition of vinylaluminum bonds to alkynes (Eq. 5–86) proceed stereospecifically:

[85] (a) E. A. Braude and J. A. Coles, *J. Chem. Soc.*, **1951**, 2078, 2085; (b) D. Y. Curtin and J. W. Crump, *J. Am. Chem. Soc.*, **80**, 1922 (1958).

$$(C_6H_5)_3Sn\!-\!\overset{H}{\underset{}{C}}\!\!=\!\!\overset{H}{\underset{}{C}}CH_3 + C_6H_5Li \longrightarrow (C_6H_5)_4Sn + Li\!-\!\overset{H}{\underset{}{C}}\!\!=\!\!\overset{H}{\underset{}{C}}CH_3 \quad (5\text{-}85)^{86}$$

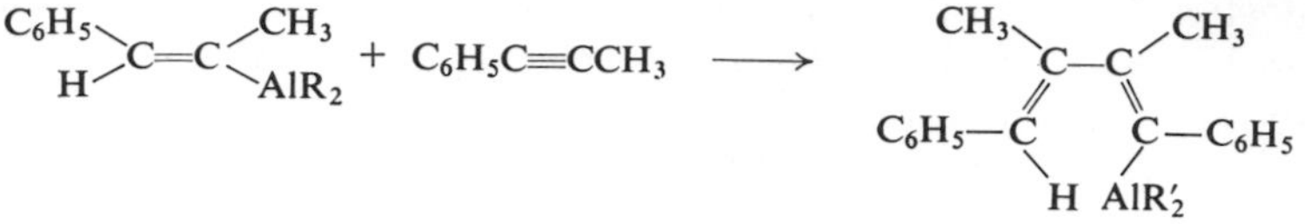

$$\underset{H}{\overset{C_6H_5}{>}}C\!=\!C\underset{AlR_2}{\overset{CH_3}{<}} + C_6H_5C\!\equiv\!CCH_3 \longrightarrow$$

(5-86)[87]

Rates and Equilibria as a Function of Organic Group in R_mM

In reactions where the R group of the reagent R_mM is not incorporated into the desired organic product, the nature of R may be chosen for rate or equilibrium advantage. This situation obtains in preparing other organo-metallics (R′M) by metal–hydrogen, metal–halogen, metal–metal, or metal hydride–olefin exchanges. Ease of attaining the foregoing transition-state configurations makes the rates of many reactions strongly dependent on R in R_mM (Eqs. 5-87 and 5-88). Furthermore, not only may certain reactions reach equilibrium at greater conversion with a given RM (Eq. 5-89), but a shift in the equilibrium by precipitation or volatilization of one of the products may be more feasible (Eqs. 5-90 and 5-91). Therefore, the most useful

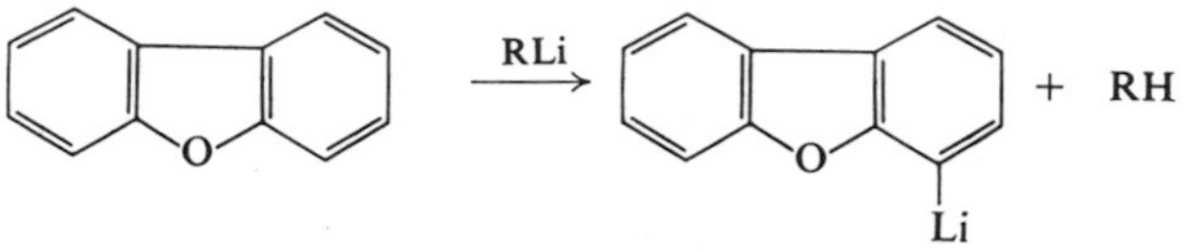

$$+ \quad RH \qquad (5\text{-}87)^{88}$$

$$R = n\text{-}C_4H_9 = 76\%$$
$$R = C_6H_5 = 31\%$$

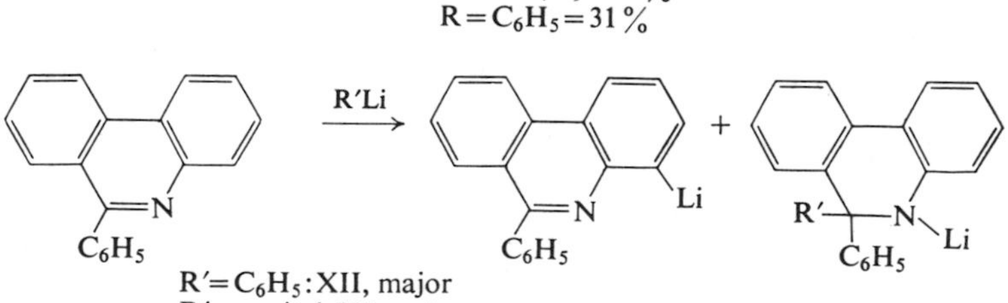

$$R' = C_6H_5 : XII, \text{ major}$$
$$R' = \text{mesityl} : XI, \text{ major}$$

XI   XII

(5-88)[89]

[86] D. Seyferth and L. G. Vaughan, *J. Am. Chem. Soc.*, **86**, 883 (1964).

[87] J. J. Eisch and W. C. Kaska, *J. Am. Chem. Soc.*, **88**, 2213 (1966).

[88] H. Gilman, F. W. Moore, and O. Baine, *J. Am. Chem. Soc.*, **63**, 2479 (1941).

[89] (a) H. Gilman and R. D. Nelson, *J. Am. Chem. Soc.*, **70**, 3316 (1948); (b) J. J. Eisch and R. M. Thompson, *J. Org. Chem.*, **27**, 4171 (1962).

$$\underset{\text{Br}}{\bigcirc} + CH_3CH_2CH_2CH_2Li \rightleftharpoons \underset{\text{Li}}{\bigcirc} + CH_3CH_2CH_2CH_2Br \quad (5\text{-}89)^{90}$$

$$(CH_3CH_2)_3Al + (C_6H_5CH_2)_3B \rightleftharpoons (C_6H_5CH_2)_3Al + (CH_3CH_2)_3B \quad (5\text{-}90)^{91}$$

$$[(CH_3)_2CHCH_2]_3Al + 3C_6H_5(CH_3)C{=}CH_2 \rightleftharpoons [C_6H_5(CH_3)CHCH_2]_3Al + 3(CH_3)_2C{=}CH_2\uparrow$$
$$(5\text{-}91)^{92}$$

variations in R will be (a) to change the group weight of R to permit driving the reaction to equilibrium by removing a product; (b) to vary saturation in R for rate or equilibrium advantage (sequence of decreasing nucleophilic activity and increasing carbanionic stability: alkyl > vinyl ~ phenyl > alkinyl); and (c) to enhance or diminish the steric requirements of R and thereby to foster one of several possible modes of reaction (Eqs. 5–67, 5–68, and 5–88).

UNSTABLE INTERMEDIATES

In many interesting organometallic reactions, the final products bear no obvious relationship to the previous types of chemical change. An insight into these transformations requires the detection and isolation of unstable intermediates which are the real precursors of the final products. Furthermore, in certain cases for which a formal mechanism can be proposed, closer scrutiny reveals that isolable complexes are the actual reacting species. Although the intimate details of many reactions are as yet unknown and the catalog of existing data is too extensive to be treated here in full scope, it seems desirable to cite the types of transitory chemical species encountered in organometallic systems. As metals, and indeed even metalloids, are centers of Lewis acidity and as most co-reactants are Lewis bases of some type, the preliminary formation of complexes in many organometallic reactions is to be expected ($R_2C{=}O \rightarrow MR'X$ and $R_3Al \leftarrow Cl—MCl$). Whether these complexes are genuine precursors to the reaction proper or are merely diverted reactants in equilibrium with more active components must be established for individual cases. In the reaction of amines with triphenylaluminum[93] the complex isolable at low temperatures undergoes elimination of benzene at 180–230°:

$$(C_6H_5)_3Al + :NH_2CH_3 \longrightarrow (C_6H_5)_3\overset{\ominus}{Al}—\overset{\oplus}{N}H_2CH_3 \xrightarrow[-C_6H_6]{> 180°} [C_6H_5Al—NCH_3]_x \quad (5\text{-}92)$$

[90] H. Gilman, W. Langham, and F. W. Moore, *J. Am. Chem. Soc.*, **62**, 2327 (1940).
[91] R. Köster and G. Bruno, *Ann.*, **629**, 89 (1960).
[92] K. Ziegler, F. Krupp, and K. Zosel, *Ann.*, **629**, 241 (1960).
[93] A. W. Laubengayer, K. Wade, and G. Lengnick, *Inorg. Chem.*, **1**, 632 (1962).

A closely related situation is a reaction formally resembling a metal-metal exchange (RM + M′X → RM′ + MX], but whose products are hydrocarbons and lower oxidation states of M′. This type of reaction is commonly observed in attempts to prepare ordinary alkyl derivatives of transition metals. Thus, the treatment of $TiCl_4$, with RLi, RMgX, or R_3Al at ordinary temperatures yields a mixture of alkanes, alkenes, $TiCl_2$, and $TiCl_3$.[94] Since by judicious choice of RM, transition metal salt, solvent, and (low) temperature, one has been able to detect and characterize labile transition metal alkyls[95] and complexes, it seems justified in assuming that decompositions observed in attempted metal-metal exchanges proceed through labile alkyl intermediates:

$$R_3Al + TiCl_4 \longrightarrow [R_3Al \cdot TiCl_4] \longrightarrow [R_2AlCl \cdot RTiCl_3]$$

$$\xrightarrow[-R_2AlCl]{} RTiCl_3 \longrightarrow R \cdot + TiCl_3 \qquad (5\text{-}93)$$

In appropriate circumstances, the group R does not dissociate completely from the transition metal, but it rather now establishes a more stable type of bonding. Thus when $CrCl_3$ is treated with phenyllithium in tetrahydrofuran solution, the σ-bonded $(C_6H_5)_3Cr \cdot 3C_4H_8O$ is formed in an isolable state.[96] When the reaction is conducted in the presence of ethyl ether, however, decomposition and rearrangement give chiefly the π-bonded sandwich complexes of bisbenzenechromium(I) salts[97] (Eq. 5–94). From these examples

$$CrCl_3 \quad \xrightarrow[\text{2. } H_3O^{\oplus}]{\text{1. } C_6H_5MgBr} \quad \overset{\displaystyle \langle \text{ring} \rangle \text{—R}}{\underset{\displaystyle \text{R—}\langle \text{ring} \rangle}{Cr^+}} \quad R = H, C_6H_5 \qquad (5\text{-}94)$$

it is apparent that the "abnormal" reactions of Grignard reagents catalyzed by transition metal salts may involve unstable σ- or π-bonded transition metal organometallics. The ability of combinations of Groups IA–IIIA alkyls and transition metal compounds to polymerize olefins (Ziegler-Natta catalysts) almost certainly depends upon such unstable intermediates. Possibly σ-alkyl-transition metal bonds can insert olefins π-complexed to the same metal center (XIII, Eq. 5–95). The stereoregularity of these polymerizations could be ascribed to asymmetric induction, as has been discussed earlier, arising from monomer accessibility to the hetereogeneous catalyst surface or simple

[94] (a) H. Gilman, R. G. Jones, and L. A. Woods, *J. Am. Chem. Soc.*, **76**, 3615 (1964); (b) R. O. C. Norman and W. A. Waters, *J. Chem. Soc.*, **1957**, 950, have detected free alkyl radicals in the interaction of Grignard reagents with cobalt(II) chloride.

[95] H. Bestian and K. Clauss, *Angew. Chem.*, **75**, 1068 (1963).

[96] W. Herwig and H. H. Zeiss, *J. Am. Chem. Soc.*, **79**, 6561 (1957).

[97] H. H. Zeiss and W. Herwig, *J. Am. Chem. Soc.*, **78**, 5959 (1956).

$$ \text{XIII} \qquad\qquad (5\text{–}95) $$

steric hindrance for homogeneous catalysts (cf. References 98 and 99). Also in the Reppe processes for the transformations of acetylene, the prominence of transition metal catalysis points to the intervention of organometallic π-complexes as the reactive species. Recent investigations on the extension of Ziegler-Natta catalysis to alkynes and 1,3-dienes have provided abundant and fruitful support of this view.[100, 101] Especially revealing have been the stereoselective dimerization and trimerization of 1,3-butadiene by various transition metal salts combined with organoaluminum compounds. Stoichiometric complexes such as XIV (π-allylic) and XV have been isolated and found to catalyze the dimerization and trimerization, respectively, of butadiene.

$$ \text{XIV} \qquad\qquad \text{XV} \qquad\qquad \text{XVI} $$

Furthermore, from treating the chromium-trimerizing catalyst [CrO_2Cl_2 and $(CH_3CH_2)_3Al$] with 2-butyne an intermediate chromium π-complex (XVI) could be isolated.[102]

Finally, organometallic reactions may involve C—M bond cleavages in a manner differing from a simple homolytic and heterolytic path. Interesting reactive intermediates can result. First, the electrolysis, radiolysis, or pyrolysis of metal alkyls may produce interesting excited free radicals[103] (Eq. 5–96). Second, the solvolysis of certain mixed metal alkyls may generate extremely

[98] W. P. Long and D. S. Breslow, *J. Am. Chem. Soc.*, **82**, 1953 (1960).
[99] D. J. Cram and K. R. Kopecky, *J. Am. Chem. Soc.*, **81**, 2748 (1959).
[100] G. N. Schrauzer et al., *Angew. Chem.*, **76**, 28 (1964).
[101] G. Wilke, *Angew. Chem.*, **75**, 10 (1963).
[102] G. Wilke and M. Kröner, *Angew. Chem.*, **71**, 574 (1959).
[103] B. G. Gowenlock and J. Trotman, *J. Chem. Soc.*, **1957**, 2114.

"hot" carbonium ions[104] (Eq. 5–97). Third, thermal treatment of metal alkyls may lead to alkylmetal hydride intermediates[105] (Eq. 5–98). And fourth, substituted metal alkyls may undergo facile α- or α,β-eliminations to form carbene or benzyne intermediates[106] (Eq. 5–99). The ability to trap the suspected intermediate in a unique chemical fashion is often taken as strong evidence for its presence. However, physical measurements such as electron spin resonance spectroscopy for odd-electron species may be necessary in ambiguous cases.

$$RHgX \xrightarrow{\text{electrolysis}} [RHg\cdot] \longrightarrow R_2Hg + Hg \qquad (5\text{–}96)$$

$$(CH_3)_3C\!-\!Hg\!-\!OAc \xrightarrow{H_3O^\oplus} [(CH_3)_3C^\oplus] + Hg^\circ \qquad (5\text{–}97)$$

$$[(CH_3)_2CHCH_2]_3B \xrightarrow{\Delta} [(CH_3)_2CHCH_2]_2BH + (CH_3)_2C\!=\!CH_2 \qquad (5\text{–}98)$$

$$(C_6H_5)_2C\!=\!CHCl \xrightarrow{RLi} (C_6H_5)_2C\!=\!CLiCl \longrightarrow [(C_6H_5)_2C\!:] \qquad (5\text{–}99)$$

[104] F. R. Jensen and R. J. Ouellette, *J. Am. Chem. Soc.*, **83**, 4477, 4478 (1961); **85**, 363, 367 (1963).
[105] R. Köster, G. Bruno, and P. Binger, *Ann.*, **644**, 1 (1961).
[106] W. Kirmse, *Carbene Chemistry*, Academic, New York, 1964, Chap. 4.

SIX

Interconversion of Organometallic Compounds

General Preparative Considerations

The basic organometallic reagents formed from the free metals and organic compounds (Chapter Two) can be transformed into different metal alkyls by several versatile routes. In this chapter the emphasis will be on the preparative feasibility of these carbon-metal bond interconversions. If the parallel between metal alkyls and metal hydrides again is advocated, then practical methods of passing from metal hydrides to the related metal alkyls deserve our attention here also. In general, a new carbon-metal bond can arise from a reagent RM by a process of substitution, addition, elimination, displacement, or rearrangement. Because of wide variations in organometallic reactivity depending upon both the metal and the organic group, the feasible synthesis of a specific metal alkyl by all five approaches usually is not possible. Furthermore, considerations such as the desired purity and quantity of the metal alkyl needed will determine the choice of the actual preparative method. A review of the classical preparative methods for the synthesis of individual metal alkyls has appeared.[1] To judge the practicality of a given organometallic preparation has demanded a careful study of the original literature and a considerable amount of laboratory work. The recent appearance of compilations of reliable procedures for organometallic compounds[2] should make the task less formidable.

[1] R. G. Jones and H. Gilman, *Chem. Rev.*, **54**, 835 (1954).
[2] J. J. Eisch and R. B. King, *Organometallic Syntheses*, Vol. 1, Academic, New York, 1965.

Some comments on the broad experimental features of a successful organo-metallic preparation are in order. In the first place, such reactions usually involve a metal alkyl as reactant or product that is sensitive to oxygen and to protic solvents. Consequently, the reaction proper, as well as transfer and purification steps, must be conducted under an atmosphere of scrupulously pure and dry nitrogen or argon. It follows that all reagents and solvents must be similarly free of such contaminants. Second, the metal alkyl reagents (for example, Grignard reagents) and other reactants (for example, main group metal halides) should be free of significant amounts of transition metal salts. Modest amounts of the latter can drastically alter the nature of the products, leading to isomeric metal alkyls or purely organic side products. Third, the donor character of the solvent can determine the success or failure of an envisioned organometallic preparation. The advantage of tetrahydrofuran over diethyl ether in the preparation of triphenylchromium (as its *tris*-tetra-hydrofuranate) was cited in Chapter Five. Strongly donating ligands apparently serve to maintain a certain stable coordination state of a given transition metal. In other situations a donor medium might be unnecessary for success, and indeed undesirable for other reasons. The preparation of Group III alkyls in an ether or amine medium illustrates this situation. The isolated products would be rather stable solvates, $R_3M \leftarrow B$, and would have to be treated further if the unsolvated alkyls were desired. Fourth, the order of reagent mixing (A added to B, or vice versa) and the stoichiometric ratio becomes most crucial in the synthesis of mixed alkyls (R_mMZ_{n-m}). Finally, the energy input into a reaction (thermal, photochemical, radiational, or electrical) can be decisive as to the isolation of labile organometallics.

Substitution

METAL-METAL EXCHANGE

Undoubtedly the most ramified type of organometallic interconversion is that of substitution. This encompasses the metal-hydrogen, metal-halogen, and metal-metal exchange reactions, and of these the latter is the most widely applicable. In equation 6–1 the starting metal alkyl R_nM is the alkylating agent, and its coreactant may be a metal salt, $M'Z_m$ or another organometallic compound (Z = X, R', OR', H, acetylacetonate):

$$mR_nM + nM'Z_m \rightleftharpoons nR_mM' + mMZ_n \qquad (6-1)$$

The position of any possible equilibrium is such as to favor the formation of the less reactive metal alkyl, R_mM', and the more ionic product, MZ_n. By this is meant that if $X_M < X_{M'}$, then usually MZ_n will be more ionic. For cases where Z is another organic group, it will usually possess a greater anionic stability and thus will tend to pair up with the more electropositive metal M. In applying this method for preparative purposes, it is well to remember that all the alkyl groups in R_nM may not be readily exchanged or that even the individual reaction steps may not go to completion. Consequently, one should choose as electropositive a metal in the alkylating agent as possible (RMgX, RLi, and RNa). In addition, by choice of the ligand Z in $M'Z_m$ one can drive the equilibrium to the right by precipitating[3] (Eq. 6–2) or by volatilizing[4] (Eq. 6–3) one of the products. In other situations unfavorable equilibria or interfering organometallic complexes may be broken up by the introduction of complexing agents[5]:

$$R_2AlCl + RBCl_2 \xleftarrow{\;BCl_3\;} R_3Al \xrightarrow{\;BF_3\;} R_3B + AlF_3\downarrow \qquad (6\text{–}2)^3$$

$$(C_2H_5)_3Al + (C_6H_5)_3B \xrightarrow{\;80°\;} (C_6H_5)_3Al + (C_2H_5)_3B\uparrow \qquad (6\text{–}3)^4$$

$$(CH_3CH_2)_3Ga \xleftarrow{\;\;\;} GaCl_3 + 3(CH_3CH_2)_3Al \xrightarrow{\;3KCl\;} (CH_3CH_2)_3Ga$$
$$+ \qquad\qquad\qquad\qquad\qquad\qquad\qquad\qquad\qquad + \qquad\qquad (6\text{–}4)^5$$
$$3(CH_3CH_2)_2AlCl \xrightarrow{\;GaCl_3\;} GaCl_3 \cdot 3(CH_3CH_2)_2AlCl \qquad 3K[Al(CH_2CH_3)_2Cl_2]$$

Either reactant-substrate complexation, as in the foregoing, or reactant-product complexation may interfere with complete alkyl transfer. Often the complexing or solvating character of the reaction medium is influential, both in accelerating the rate of such exchanges and in stabilizing the resultant product. As mentioned above, basic solvents such as Group VA and Group VIA alkyl derivatives are the most effective. Instances of this favorable effect are the synthesis of transition metal alkyls as solvates with phosphines[6] (I) and arsines[7] (II):

$$(C_6H_5)_2Ni[P(C_2H_5)_3]_2$$

I   II

The synthesis of metal alkyls containing different ligands about the metal center may be achieved from metal salts by controlling the ratio of reactants.

[3] R. Köster, *Ann.*, **618**, 31 (1958).
[4] R. Köster and G. Bruno, *Ann.*, **629**, 89 (1960).
[5] J. J. Eisch, *J. Am. Chem. Soc.*, **84**, 3605 (1962).
[6] J. Chatt and B. L. Shaw, *J. Chem. Soc.*, **1960**, 1718.
[7] G. Calvin and G. E. Coates, *J. Chem. Soc.*, **1960**, 2008.

Feasible control requires that the rates for the successive alkylation steps be sufficiently different and that the unsymmetrical product formed, RR'M', be reasonably stable to disproportionation:

$$3(CH_3)_2CHLi + SiCl_4 \rightarrow [(CH_3)_2CH]_3SiCl + 3LiCl \qquad (6-5)[8]$$

$$C_6H_5Li + [(CH_3)_2CH]_3SiCl \rightarrow [(CH_3)_2CH]_3SiC_6H_5 + LiCl \qquad (6-6)$$

In cases where such conditions do not obtain, the attempted alkylation and product isolation will yield a distribution of metal alkyls:

$$PCl_3 + (CH_3CH_2)_3Al \longrightarrow (CH_3CH_2)_xPCl_{3-x} + (CH_3CH_2)_2AlCl \qquad (6-7)[9]$$

$$(CH_3CHCH_2)_2B{-}F \xrightarrow[CH_3MgBr]{} (CH_3CHCH_2)_2B{-}CH_3 \xrightarrow{60°} (CH_3CHCH_2)_3B$$
$$\quad\; | \qquad\qquad\qquad\qquad\quad\; | \qquad\qquad\qquad\qquad | $$
$$\;\, CH_3 \qquad\qquad\qquad\qquad CH_3 \qquad\qquad\qquad\; CH_3 \qquad (6-8)[10]$$
$$\qquad\qquad\qquad\qquad\qquad\qquad\qquad\qquad\qquad\qquad +$$
$$\qquad\qquad\qquad\qquad\qquad\qquad\qquad\qquad\qquad (CH_3)_3B$$

The preceding disproportionation of an unsymmetrical boron alkyl brings up a special case of the metal-metal exchange, namely, the situation where both the metal centers involved are identical:

$$R_mM + R_m'M \underset{B}{\overset{A}{\rightleftharpoons}} R_{m-x}R_x'M$$

Reaction A is usually termed a redistribution process, whereas reaction B is designated as a disproportionation or symmetrization. Depending upon the mobility of the equilibrium, the point of equilibrium and the relative volatility of the products, such systems can be manipulated for synthetic purposes. The preparation of alkylmetal halides and the reaction of aluminum alkyls with olefins typify two valuable applications of such equilibria:

$$2(CH_3CH_2)_3Ga + GaCl_3 \xrightarrow{\Delta} 3(CH_3CH_2)_2GaCl \qquad (6-9)[5]$$

$$(C_6H_5)_4Sn + SnCl_4 \xrightarrow{\Delta} 2(C_6H_5)_2SnCl_2 \qquad (6-10)[11]$$

[8] H. Gilman and R. N. Clark, *J. Am. Chem. Soc.*, **69**, 1499 (1947).
[9] O. J. Ochlobystin and L. I. Zakharkin, *Izv. Akad. Nauk SSSR*, **1958**, 1006; through *C.A.*, **53**, 1122 (1959).
[10] G. F. Hennion, P. A. McCusker, and A. J. Rutkowski, *J. Am. Chem. Soc.*, **80**, 617 (1958).
[11] A. Goddard, J. N. Ashley, and R. B. Evans, *J. Chem. Soc.*, **1922**, 121, 981.

$$3(CH_3CH_2)_3Al + 6nCH_2{=}CH_2 \longrightarrow 3CH_3CH_2{-}Al[(CH_2CH_2)_nCH_2CH_3]_2 \qquad (6{-}11)^{12}$$

$$\downarrow \Delta$$

$$(CH_3CH_2)_3Al + 2[CH_3CH_2(CH_2CH_2)_n]_3Al$$

The attainment of a smooth metal-metal exchange calls for careful regulation of experimental conditions to achieve maximum yield of pure product. As suggested above, the alkylating agent should be an active R_nM type, easily accessible, yielding a readily separable by-product, MZ_m, and giving a minimum of side products. The metal alkyls of greatest utility, therefore, are those of lithium, sodium, potassium, magnesium, calcium, boron, and aluminum. Furthermore, the substrate $M'Z_m$ should contain the desired metal center allied with a ligand most suitable for prompt reaction, ease of separation, high solubility of the substrate, and complete exchange. The nature of Z in successful exchanges can vary widely:

$$\overset{O}{\underset{|}{}} \qquad \overset{O}{\underset{\|}{}}$$

$$H, Cl, Br, I, OR, NR_2, CH_3C{=}CH{-}C{-}CH_3, \text{ or } R$$

Moreover, the solvent medium chosen can effect profoundly both the rate and the equilibrium point of the exchange. Solvents of the hydrocarbon (alkanes and aromatics), amine (R_3N), and ether types $[R_2O, RO{-}CH_2{-}CH_2{-}OR)]$ are most often employed. Sometimes the necessity of freeing the R_nM type generated from complexing solvent and of avoiding chemical attack on the solvent will also govern the choice. In this regard, the variable of temperature deserves some comment. Often, because of steric retardation of exchange, alkylation may proceed at a disappointingly slow rate. Consequently, the use of an excess of R_nM in high concentration and/or the use of elevated temperature may prove necessary. The higher temperatures may be attained by removal of all solvent and by "baking" the solvent-free reactants, or by recourse to a higher-boiling solvent. The Grignard synthesis of phenylsilanes[13] is a case in point:

$$4C_6H_5MgBr + SiCl_4 \xrightarrow{160-180°} (C_6H_5)_4Si + SiBr_nCl_{4-n} \qquad (6{-}12)$$

On the other hand, in the synthesis of certain organometallic cyclic compounds[14] the advantages accruing from favoring the intramolecular reaction (cyclization) by working in dilute solution should be evident:

---

[12] K. Ziegler, H.-G. Gellert, K. Zosel, E. Holzkamp, J. Schneider, M. Söll, and W.-R. Kroll, *Ann.*, **629**, 121 (1960).

[13] N. W. Cusa and F. S. Kipping, *J. Chem. Soc.*, **1933**, 1040.

[14] K. Ziegler, *Angew. Chem.*, **68**, 721 (1956).

$$R_2Al-(CH_2)_4CH=CH_2 \xrightarrow{\Delta} \text{[cyclopentane with }{}^H \text{ and } CH_2AlR_2]} \qquad (6\text{-}13)$$

Some of the most common competing reactions, besides the previously mentioned ones of disproportionation, incomplete alkylation, reactant-substrate or reactant-product complexation, and solvent attack, are summarized in the following equations:

a. Metal alkyl product decomposition:

$$2CH_3MgX + NiX_2 \xrightarrow[\text{ether}]{} 2MgX_2 + [(CH_3)_2Ni] \longrightarrow Ni^\circ + C_2H_6 \qquad (6\text{-}14)[15]$$

$$(CH_3CH_2)_3Al + TlCl_4 \rightarrow (CH_3CH_2)_2AlCl + CH_3CH_2TlCl_3 \rightarrow CH_3CH_3 + TiCl_3$$
$$+ CH_2=CH_2$$
$$(6\text{-}15)[16]$$

b. Addition to unsaturated linkages:

$$(C_6H_5)_3Sn-CH=CH_2 + C_6H_5Li \rightarrow (C_6H_5)_4Sn + CH_2=CHLi \qquad (6\text{-}16)[17]$$

But,

$$(C_6H_5)_3Si-CH=CH_2 + C_6H_5Li \rightarrow (C_6H_5)_3Si-CHLi-CH_2C_6H_5 \qquad (6\text{-}17)[18]$$

c. Competing metal-hydrogen and metal-metal exchanges:

$$C_6H_5Li + \qquad \longrightarrow \qquad (6\text{-}18)[19,20]$$

d. Rearrangements:

$$4CH_3\underset{\underset{MgX}{|}}{CH}CH_3 + SiCl_4 \xrightarrow{TiCl_4} (CH_3CH_2CH_2)_nSi(CH(CH_3)_2)_{4-n} \qquad (6\text{-}19)[21]$$

[15] H. Gilman, R. G. Jones, and L. A. Woods, *J. Am. Chem. Soc.*, **76**, 3615 (1954).
[16] (a) K. Clauss and C. Beermann, *Angew. Chem.*, **71**, 627 (1959); (b) C. Beermann and H. Bestian, *ibid.*, **71**, 618 (1959).
[17] D. Seyferth and M. A. Weiner, *J. Am. Chem. Soc.*, **83**, 3583 (1961).
[18] L. F. Cason and H. G. Brooks, *J. Am. Chem. Soc.*, **74**, 4582 (1952); *J. Org. Chem.*, **19**, 1278 (1954).
[19] H. Gilman and J. W. Morton, Jr., in *Organic Reactions*, Vol. VIII (R. Adams, ed.), Wiley, New York, 1954, p. 258.
[20] R. G. Jones and H. Gilman, in *Organic Reactions*, Vol. VI (R. Adams, ed.), Wiley, New York, 1951, p. 339.
[21] H. L. Finkbeiner and G. D. Cooper, *J. Org. Chem.*, **26**, 4779 (1961).

METAL-HYDROGEN EXCHANGE[19]

Commonly known as metalation, this reaction offers a unique approach to new types of carbon-metal linkages. Since the replaceable hydrogen can be considered to exhibit positive character, this process can be correlated with the pseudoacidic character of hydrogen-containing organic compounds (cf. Chapter Four):

$$R_nM + {}_nH{-}R' \rightleftharpoons R_{n}'M + {}_nH{-}R \qquad (6{-}20)$$

From a thermodynamic viewpoint, the foregoing equilibrium lies on the side of the weaker acid, H—R, and the more stable salt, $R_{n}'M$. From a kinetic standpoint, the most efficient metalating agents are alkyls of alkali and alkaline earth metals, although compounds of mercury, aluminum, and boron do qualify for special applications. Indeed, the site in the organic substrate which a given R_nM type will metalate can vary with the nature of the reagent and the experimental conditions. For by reason of varying mechanistic pathways the product can be determined by thermodynamic or by kinetic control. The ensuing equations help to indicate the scope of metalative preparations:

$$(C_6H_5)_3Al + C_6H_5{-}C{\equiv}C{-}H \longrightarrow (C_6H_5)_2Al{-}C{\equiv}C{-}C_6H_5 + C_6H_6 \qquad (6{-}21)[22]$$

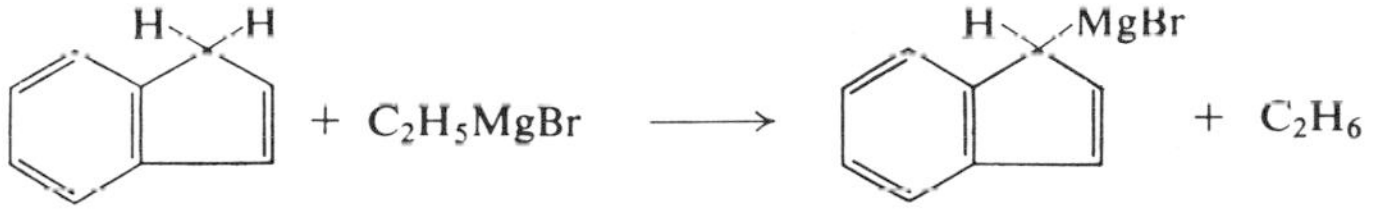

$$+ \ C_2H_5MgBr \longrightarrow \qquad + \ C_2H_6 \qquad (6{-}22)[19]$$

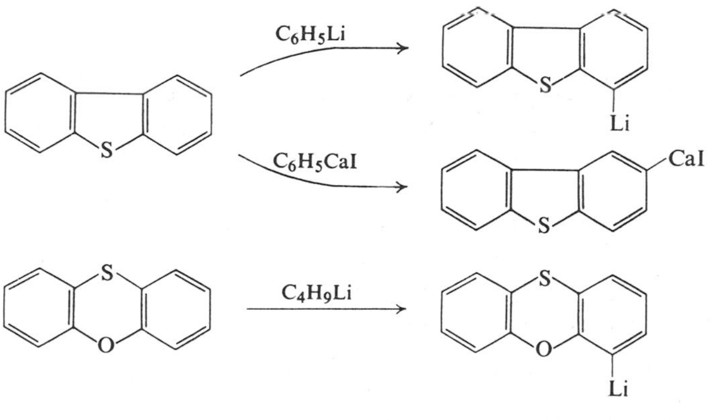

$(6{-}23)[19]$

$(6{-}24)[23]$

$(6{-}25)[19]$

[22] J. J. Eisch and W. C. Kaska, *J. Organometal. Chem. (Amsterdam)*, **2**, 184 (1964).
[23] H. Gilman, A. L. Jacoby, and H. A. Pacevitz, *J. Org. Chem.*, **3**, 120 (1938).

$$+ \ C_6H_6 \qquad (6\text{–}26)^{24}$$

$$X = F, O\text{—}R \qquad (6\text{–}27)^{25}$$

With the metalating agents (RM) of Group I the thermodynamic basicity of the carbanion $R^\ominus$ varies in the expected order: $\diagdown C^\ominus > \diagdown C\!=\!C^{\diagup\ominus} > -C\!\equiv\!C^\ominus$, and among isomeric alkyl groups: $R_3C^\ominus > R_2CH^\ominus > RCH_2{}^\ominus$. However, with the reactive saline alkyls, RNa, RK, etc., the products resulting from metalations of short contact times often may be the kinetically controlled[26]:

reaction time:		percentage	
3 hr	42	39	19
20 hr	88	4	8

The reactivity of a metalating agent (RM) usually stands in the reverse order of its carbanionic stability. Hence, the reactivity varies, alkyl > aryl > alkynyl. However, it is not always of advantage to employ the most reactive metalating agents, as, for example, *n*-amylsodium, for several reasons. First, the metalation of isopropylbenzene by *n*-amylpotassium (Eq. 6–28) exposes the uncontrolled and variable nature of the metalation products, when kinetic and thermodynamic control compete. Second, the reactivity of certain alkyls leads to attack upon many reaction solvents and hence destruction of the alkyl under the metalating conditions. Such solvent attack is encountered with just those reaction media (ethers and tertiary amines)

[24] J. J. Eisch and W. C. Kaska, *J. Am. Chem. Soc.*, **84**, 1501 (1962).
[25] Cf. R. Huisgen in *Organometallic Chemistry* (H. H. Zeiss, ed.), Reinhold, New York, 1960, pp. 36–87, for a review of organometallic approaches to benzyne chemistry.
[26] R. A. Benkeser, J. Hooz, T. V. Liston, and A. B. Trevillan, *J. Am. Chem. Soc.*, **85**, 3984 (1963),

which *enhance* the rates of desired metalations. Third, as is discussed later, reactive alkyls often will allow undesired side reactions to assume discouraging proportions. Consequently, the less reactive, ethereal solutions of lithium alkyls and aryls are frequently utilized, since they are versatile, selective, and fairly rapid metalating agents whose ether solutions are feasibly stable. The ether instability and insolubility of phenylsodium has been circumvented by preparing more stable, yet highly reactive, 1:1 complexes with phenyl-lithium.[27] It is true that the maximal extent of metalation may not be reached due to competing solvent attack. As already suggested, donor solvents (ethers such as tetrahydrofuran and glycol dimethyl ether and tertiary amines such as N-methylpyrrolidine and tetramethylethylenediamine) increase the rate of metalation over that observed in hydrocarbon media.[28] There is some evidence that metal salts (lithium piperidide[29] and sodium alkoxides[30]) function as metalation catalysts.

The range of metalating behavior depicted in Eqs. 6–21 to 6–27 can be viewed formally as the result of S_E2 attack on unsaturated carbon by M^I, or as S_N2 attack on pseudoacidic hydrogen by R^-. A more substantiated analysis of mechanism awaits further research into the behavior of the various metal alkyls. When the organic compound offers active methylene protons, these are the principal sites of attack in such S_N2 processes by carbanions or cryptocarbanions. In general, the acidity scales of Conant-Wheland-McEwen[31] determine the direction of proton transfer.

With vinyl and aryl systems there is a tendency for metalation adjacent to the electronegative group[19]:

$$(6\text{–}29)$$

By carefully conceived appending of the metalating agent to a side chain, metalation of more distant positions can be achieved[32]:

[27] G. Wittig and E. Benz, *Ber.*, **91**, 873 (1958).
[28] H. Gilman and S. Gray, *J. Org. Chem.*, **23**, 1476 (1958).
[29] (a) R. Huisgen in *Organometallic Chemistry* (H. H. Zeiss, ed.), Reinhold, New York, 1960, p. 36; (b) J. J. Eisch and W. C. Kaska, *J. Org. Chem.*, **27**, 3745 (1962).
[30] A. A. Morton, C. E. Claff, and F. W. Collins, *J. Org. Chem.*, **20**, 428 (1955).
[31] (a) J. B. Conant and G. W. Wheland, *J. Am. Chem. Soc.*, **54**, 1212 (1932); (b) W. K. McEwen, *ibid.*, **58**, 1124 (1936); (c) D. J. Cram, *Fundamentals of Carbanion Chemistry*, Benjamin, New York, 1965.
[32] J. J. Eisch and M. E. Healey, *J. Am. Chem. Soc.*, **86**, 4221 (1964).

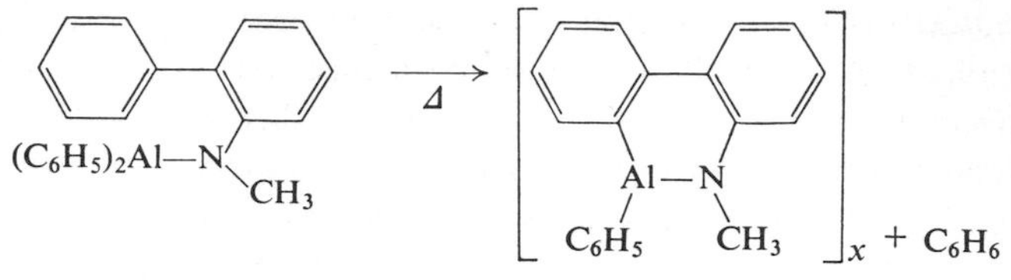

$$(6\text{-}30)$$

An increase of attack at the para position of phenyl derivatives may be promoted by the use of bulky metalating agents[33]:

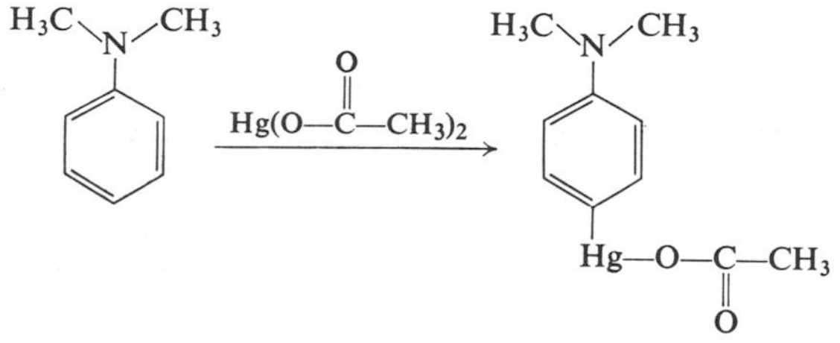

$$(6\text{-}31)$$

In instances where addition to an unsaturated linkage can occur, a bulky agent could retard addition without interfering with the desired metalation[34]:

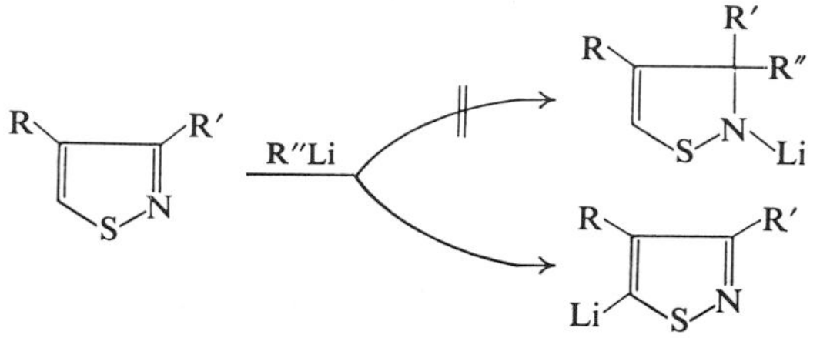

$$R'' = 2\text{-biphenylyl}$$

$$(6\text{-}32)$$

Despite one's best efforts in choosing the metalating agent and experimental conditions, undesirable side reactions can abound. As seen above, isomeric metalation products and solvent cleavage products usually intrude, together with addition products of $C{=}E$ linkages. Therefore, the resultant metal derivative may be formed only in modest yield (25–50%) and admixed with tediously separable impurities. Nevertheless, that the metalation reaction offers access to organometallics obtainable in no other way makes this route of great value both in organic and inorganic synthesis. The uniqueness resides in its pronounced tendency to metalate *ortho* to an electronegative substituent on the benzene ring in the order, $O > S > N$.

[33] F. C. Whitmore, *J. Am. Chem. Soc.*, **41**, 1841 (1919).
[34] R. B. Woodward and G. Volpp, Harvard University, 1962, unpublished work directed to the synthesis of colchicine.

One inherent limitation for synthetic purposes, but actually a gain in another sense, is the instability of certain metalation products. The principal mode of decomposition is that of elimination (of MX, MOR, R_3N, or MH) and of ring opening: Equations 6–27 and 6–33 depict the generation of benzynes and carbenes, respectively, from the former type of decomposition. Other examples follow:

$$CH_2Cl_2 + CH_3Li \rightarrow [CHLiCl_2] \rightarrow [H—C—Cl] \qquad (6\text{-}33)^{35}$$

$$C_6H_5CH_2—O—CH_2CH_3 \xrightarrow{R—Li} C_6H_5CH_2—OLi + CH_2=CH_2 \qquad (6\text{-}34)^{36}$$

$$(CH_2)_6 \Big\langle {\overset{CH_2}{\underset{CH—N(CH_3)_3}{\big|}}} \xrightarrow{RLi} (CH_2)_6 \Big\langle {\overset{CH}{\underset{CH}{\big\|}}} + (CH_3)_3N \qquad (6\text{-}35)^{37}$$

$$\xrightarrow{C_6H_5Li} \quad + \ C_6H_6 + LiH \qquad (6\text{-}36)^{38}$$

METAL-HALOGEN EXCHANGE[20]

The metalloid character of the halogen in certain organic halides is evidenced in the metal-halogen exchange reaction (Eq. 6–37). Formally, therefore, this interconversion is closely related to metal-metal exchange,

$$RM + XR' \rightleftharpoons R'M + XR \qquad (6\text{-}37)$$

but its synthetic applications are uniquely important. As with the other exchanges, the equilibriated system favors the attachment of the more electropositive metal with the more electronegative organic group. Thus interactions between metal alkyls and aryl halides are particularly favorable for complete exchange. Although such exchanges have been observed with alkyls of lithium, sodium, magnesium, barium, and aluminum, the versatility of lithium alkyls and their lessened tendency to undergo side reactions in these metal-halogen metal exchanges are indisputable. Indeed, Grignard reagents undergo this

[35] G. L. Closs and L. E. Closs, *J. Am. Chem. Soc.*, **81**, 4996 (1959); **82**, 5723 (1960).
[36] G. Wittig and L. Lohmann, *Ann.*, **550**, 260 (1942).
[37] G. Wittig and R. Polster, *Ann.*, **612**, 102 (1958).
[38] H. Gilman and C. W. Bradley, *J. Am. Chem. Soc.*, **60**, 2333 (1938).

reaction with facility with certain compounds[39] (Eq. 6–38) or under special conditions[40] (Eq. 6–39):

$$C_6H_5C\equiv CBr + CH_3MgBr \rightarrow C_6H_5C\equiv CMgBr + CH_3Br \qquad (6-38)$$

$$(C_6H_5)_2C{=}C\overset{C_6H_5}{\underset{Br}{\diagup}} + CH_3MgBr \rightarrow (C_6H_5)_2C{=}C\overset{C_6H_5}{\underset{MgBr}{\diagup}} \ (32\%) + CH_3Br \quad (6-39)$$

The bromine and iodine groups of aryl halides are exchanged most readily and ether appears to be the most suitable reaction medium. In assessing the effectiveness of the organolithium reagent in exchanges with 1-bromo-naphthalene, the yields of 1-naphthyllithium decreased in the order: n-$C_3H_7Li > C_2H_5Li > n$-$C_4H_9Li > C_6H_5Li > CH_3Li$. The reasonable rates still attainable with n-butyllithium combine with its ready availability to make it the reagent of choice.

Not only do similarities in metal-hydrogen and metal-halogen exchange suggest a similar mechanism, but the two reactions can compete with each other in a given system. Fortunately, lithium-bromine and lithium-iodine exchanges often occur more readily than lithium-hydrogen substitutions or other addition reactions. By working at low temperatures and employing sufficient lithium alkyl to discharge any acidic hydrogens unique aryllithium derivatives can be won:

$$(6-40)^{41}$$

$$(6-41)^{42}$$

$$(6-42)^{24}$$

[39] M. S. Kharasch, F. L. Lambert, and W. H. Urry, *J. Org. Chem.*, **10**, 298 (1945).
[40] M. S. Kharasch and C. F. Fuchs, *J. Org. Chem.*, **10**, 292 (1945).
[41] H. Gilman and H. W. Melvin, Jr., unpublished studies cited in Ref. 20.
[42] H. Gilman and S. M. Spatz, *J. Org. Chem.*, **16**, 1485 (1951).

Side reactions involving metal-metal or metal-hydrogen exchanges, as well as the intended metal-halogen exchange, may lead to unstable lithium compounds. As cited above, these may undergo metal salt elimination to produce carbenes and benzynes. One additional annoyance is the slow metal-alkyl exchange that can occur between the products of a metal-halogen exchange[43]:

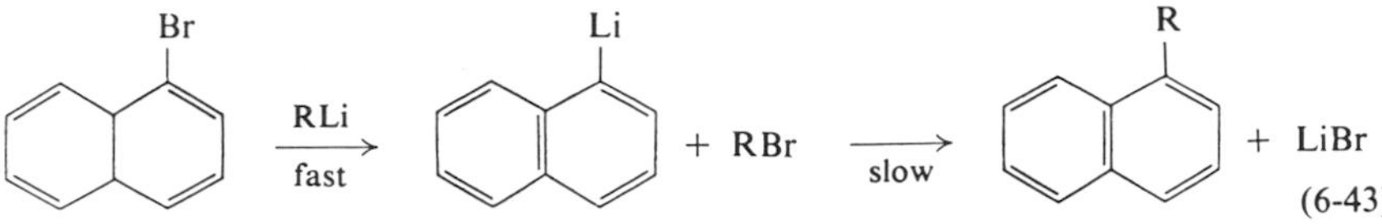

$$(6\text{-}43)$$

Addition

The two principal types of addition leading to new carbon-metal bonds are (1) the addition of metal salts MZ to an unsaturated hydrocarbon and (2) the addition of Lewis acidic organometallics to other organometallics or metal salts. In the former type, Z of MZ can be a carbon group, hydrogen, halogen, or pseudohalogen, while the unsaturated hydrocarbon substrates can be alkenes, alkynes, transient carbenes, or arynes. In the latter type of addition are included all complexes between different organometallic types ($RLi + R_3'Al$; $R_2Sn + R'Li$). Possibly the most important reaction of all these sub-types of addition is the addition of metal hydrides to unsaturated hydrocarbons. These reactions require our prime attention.

HYDROMETALATION

In general, the hydrides of Groups IA–IVA and of the coordination compounds of transition metals are able to form adducts with olefins and acetylenes:

$$(6\text{-}44)$$

As implied in the latter equation, the adduction is often feasibly reversible. Therefore, the mode of addition as to *cis* or *trans* character or as to orientation (III or IV) may be subject to kinetic[44] or thermodynamic[45] control:

[43] H. Gilman, C. G. Brannen, and R. K. Ingham, *J. Org. Chem.*, **22**, 685 (1957).
[44] G. Wilke and H. Müller, *Ann.*, **629**, 222 (1960).
[45] J. J. Eisch and W. C. Kaska, *J. Am. Chem. Soc.*, **88**, 2213 (1966).

$$R-C\equiv C-R \xrightarrow{R_2'AlH} \underset{H}{\overset{R}{>}}C=C\underset{AlR_2'}{\overset{R}{<}} \xrightarrow[\Delta]{R_2'AlH} \underset{H}{\overset{R}{>}}C=C\underset{R}{\overset{AlR_2'}{<}}$$

$$(6\text{-}45)$$

The ease of hydrometalation and the importance of side reactions vary markedly, depending upon whether a saline type (Na^+H^-) or a covalent member (R_3Pb—H) is concerned. From existing evidence it appears that both polar and radical mechanisms are operative in these hydride additions. Among the metal hydrides those of Group IA seem to hydrometalate least satisfactorily, both for kinetic and thermodynamic reasons. Nucleophilic attack by the hydride ion on unactivated olefins and acetylenes seems to be unfavorable kinetically. Proton abstraction often competes successfully (Eq. 6–46). Furthermore, the great stability of saline hydrides strongly promotes elimination [46] the reverse reaction of Eq. 6–44, (Eq. 6–47). Much

$$R-C\equiv C-H + H^{\ominus}Na^{\oplus} \longrightarrow R-C\equiv C^{\ominus}Na^{\oplus} + H_2\uparrow \qquad (6\text{-}46)$$

$$CH_3CH_2CH_2CH_2Li \xrightarrow{\Delta} CH_3CH_2CH=CH_2 + LiH \qquad (6\text{-}47)^{[46]}$$

smoother adduction occurs with Group IIA, and especially Group IIIA, hydrides. These polar, associated covalent hydrides apparently interact with unsaturated hydrocarbons in an electrophilic manner. The influence of donor solvents is most favorable on the hydroboration reaction,[47] but parallel studies for other hydrometalation reactions are lacking. On the other hand, it is reasonable to expect that highly basic media such as tertiary amines would have a decelerating effect on such additions. Although the presence of Lewis acid catalysts in such additions seems desirable, possible acid catalysis is not yet certain. Substituent effects, nevertheless, do point to a polar, rather than just a steric, control of isomeric products:

$$Cl-\underset{}{\bigcirc}-\overset{H}{\underset{}{C}}=\overset{H}{\underset{}{CH}} \xrightarrow{B_2H_6}$$

$$Cl-\bigcirc-CH_2CH_2-BH_2 + Cl-\bigcirc-\underset{BH_2}{\overset{|}{C}H}-CH_3 \qquad (6\text{-}48)^{[48]}$$
$$65\% \qquad\qquad\qquad\qquad\qquad 35\%$$

$$(CH_3CH_2)_3Si-\overset{H}{\underset{}{C}}=\overset{H}{\underset{}{CH}} \xrightarrow{R_2AlH}$$

$$(CH_3CH_2)_3SiCH_2CH_2-AlR_2 + (CH_3CH_2)_3Si\underset{AlR_2}{\overset{|}{C}}HCH_3 \qquad (6\text{-}49)^{[49]}$$
$$30\% \qquad\qquad\qquad\qquad 70\%$$

[46] K. Ziegler, *Brennstoff-Chem.*, **33**, 193 (1952).
[47] Cf. H. C. Brown, *Hydroboration*, Benjamin, New York, 1962, p. 4, *inter alia*, for the accelerating effect of ether media on borane addition to olefins.
[48] H. C. Brown and G. Zweifel, *J. Am. Chem. Soc.*, **82**, 4708 (1960).
[49] J. J. Eisch and G. R. Husk, *J. Org. Chem.*, **29**, 254 (1964).

The addition of the covalent hydrides of Group IVA to organic substrates under certain conditions would seem to involve conventional, free radical chain processes, since radical promoters (e.g., benzoyl peroxide and azo-*bis*-isobutyronitrile) and energy sources (thermal, ultraviolet light, and gamma radiation) accelerate the hydrometalation process.[50] To convey some impression of the scope of hydrometalation either by polar or radical reagents, significant examples of metal hydride adduction are presented in Table 6–1. Of extraordinary interest is the relevance of hydrometalation by cobalt hydrides to the industrial hydroformylation of olefins (oxo process) and. to the biochemistry of cobamide enzymes.

TABLE 6–1

Additions of Metal Hydrides to Olefins

Olefinic Substrate	Metal Hydride[a]	Product	Ref.
$RCH{=}CH_2$	BH_3	$(RCH_2CH_2)_3B$	b
$(CH_3)_2C{=}CH_2$	AlH_3	$[(CH_3)_2CHCH_2]_3Al$	c
$RCH{=}CH_2$	GaH_3[d]	$(RCH_2CH_2)_3Ga$	e
$RCH{=}CH_2$	InH_3[d,f]	$(RCH_2CH_2)_3In$	e, g
$RCH{=}CH_2$	Cl_3SiH	$RCH_2CH_2SiCl_3$	h
$(C_6H_5)_3GeCH_2CH{=}CH_2$	$(C_6H_5)_3GeH$	$[(C_6H_5)_3GeCH_2]_2CH_2$	i
$N{\equiv}C{-}CH{=}CH_2$	$(C_6H_5)_3SnH$	$(C_6H_5)_3SnCH_2CH_2C{\equiv}N$	j, k
$CH_2{=}CH_2$	$(CH_3)_3PbH$	$(CH_3)_3PbCH_2CH_3$	l
$CH_2{=}CH{-}CH{=}CH_2$	$(CO)_4CoH$	$(CO)_3CoCH{-}CH{=}CH_2$ $\quad\quad\quad\quad\mid$ $\quad\quad\quad\quad CH_3$	m

[a] The associated character of the metal hydrides is ignored.
[b] H. C. Brown, *Hydroboration*, Benjamin, New York, 1962.
[c] K. Ziegler et al., *Ann.*, **629**, 1 (1960).
[d] The hydride source was the isobutylmetal system.
[e] J. J. Eisch, *J. Am. Chem. Soc.*, **84**, 3830 (1962).
[f] Much decomposition of alkylindium derivatives accompanied reaction.
[g] Low yield of desired product.
[h] J. L. Speier et al., *J. Am. Chem. Soc.*, **78**, 2278 (1956).
[i] H. Gilman and C. W. Gerow, *J. Am. Chem. Soc.*, **79**, 342 (1957).
[j] G. J. M. van der Kerk et al., *Chem. Ind.* (*London*), **1956**, 352; **1958**, 609.
[k] W. P. Neumann et al., *Angew. Chem.*, **76**, 849 (1964).
[l] W. E. Becker and S. E. Cook, *J. Am. Chem. Soc.*, **82**, 6264 (1960).
[m] D. W. Moore et al., *Chem. Ind.* (*London*), **1960**, 1304; a *pi*-allylic structure is involved.

[50] C. Eaborn, *Organosilicon Compounds*, Academic, New York, 1960, p. 45.

Attention should be drawn to further particular aspects of hydrometalation. With the derivatives of the simplest alkene, methylene, or its precursors, hydrometalation leads to insertion in metal-hydrogen bonds[51]:

$$(n\text{-}C_4H_9)_3Sn\text{—H} + CH_2 \xrightarrow{(CH_2N_2)} (n\text{-}C_4H_9)_3Sn\text{—}CH_3 \qquad (6\text{-}50)$$

In the case of alkynes where *bis*-hydrometalation can be achieved, the metal atoms tend to be bonded in a *geminal* manner if a polar adduction is operative[44] (Eq. 6–51). Free radical additions tend to favor *vicinal* metal attachment[52] (Eq. 6–52). In addition, solvent can often cause a side reaction

$$R\text{—}C\equiv C\text{—}H + 2R_2'AlH \rightarrow RCH_2CH(AlR_2')_2 \qquad (6\text{-}51)$$

$$H\text{—}C\equiv C\text{—}H + 2(C_6H_5)_3SnH \rightarrow (C_6H_5)_3SnCH_2CH_2Sn(C_6H_5)_3 \qquad (6\text{-}52)$$

(metalation of acidic hydrogens) to take complete precedence over hydrometalation. The behavior of pure dialkylaluminum hydrides toward terminal alkynes[22, 44] contrasts sharply with that of the hydride in tertiary amines[53]:

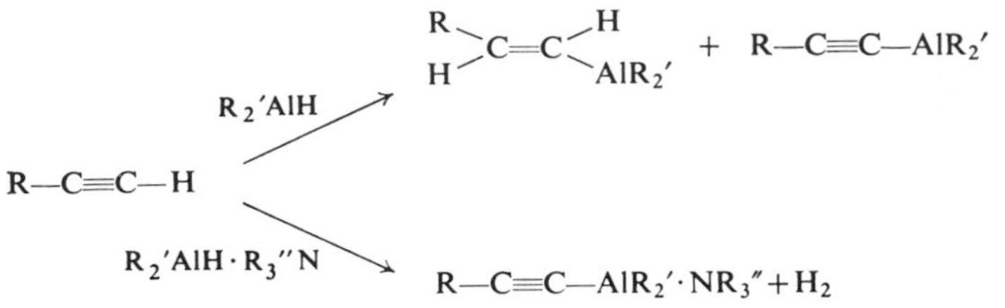

$$
R\text{—}C\equiv C\text{—}H
\begin{cases}
\xrightarrow{R_2'AlH} & \underset{H}{\overset{R}{>}}C{=}C\underset{AlR_2'}{\overset{H}{<}} \;+\; R\text{—}C\equiv C\text{—}AlR_2' \\
\xrightarrow{R_2'AlH \cdot R_3''N} & R\text{—}C\equiv C\text{—}AlR_2' \cdot NR_3'' + H_2
\end{cases}
\qquad (6\text{-}53)
$$

Finally, suitable metal alkyls, having branching at the β-carbon atom can serve as precursors for metal hydride (Eq. 6–54). Thermal elimination of a volatile alkene forms the basis for a useful olefin displacement approach to metal alkyls (Eqs. 6–54 and 6–55). The method has been applied most successfully to the preparation of aluminum,[54] boron,[55] and gallium[56] alkyls. A practical application demands that the equilibrium in Eq. 6–54 be established at a temperature where the carbon-metal bond is stable. Thus the thermolysis of carbon-indium bonds hinders the clean olefin displacement depicted below.[56]

[51] M. Lesbre, *Bull. soc. chim. France*, **1957**, 1204.
[52] G. J. M. van der Kerk and J. C. Noltes, *J. Appl. Chem.*, **9**, 106 (1959).
[53] P. Binger, *Angew. Chem.*, **75**, 918 (1963).
[54] K. Ziegler, W.-R. Kroll, W. Larbig, and O.-W. Steudel, *Ann.*, **629**, 53 (1960).
[55] R. Köster, *Angew. Chem.*, **68**, 383 (1956); **70**, 413 (1958).
[56] J. J. Eisch, *J. Am. Chem. Soc.*, **84**, 3830 (1962).

$$(CH_3CHCH_2)_3Al \rightleftharpoons (CH_3CHCH_2)_2AlH + (CH_3)_2C\!\!=\!\!CH_2\uparrow \qquad (6\text{-}54)$$
$$\underset{\displaystyle CH_3}{|} \qquad\qquad \underset{\displaystyle CH_3}{|}$$

$$(CH_3CHCH_2)_2AlH + H_2C\!\!=\!\!CHR \rightleftharpoons (CH_3CHCH_2)_2AlCH_2CH_2R \qquad (6\text{-}55)$$
$$\underset{\displaystyle CH_3}{|} \qquad\qquad\qquad\qquad \underset{\displaystyle CH_3}{|}$$

$$3(CH_3CHCH_2)_2AlCH_2CH_2R \rightarrow 2(CH_3CHCH_2)_3Al + (RCH_2CH_2)_3Al \qquad (6\text{-}56)$$
$$\underset{\displaystyle CH_3}{|} \qquad\qquad\qquad \underset{\displaystyle CH_3}{|}$$

HALOMETALATION

In order to treat the addition of metal halides or related compounds to unsaturates in this chapter, strict consistency would limit the discussion to mixed metal alkyls:

$$R_{m-1}M\!\!-\!\!X + R'\!\!-\!\!C\overset{\cdots}{=\!\!=}C\!\!-\!\!R' \rightleftharpoons R'\!\!-\!\!\underset{X}{\overset{\cdots}{C}}\!\!-\!\!\underset{MR_{m-1}}{\overset{\cdots}{C}}\!\!-\!\!R' \qquad (6\text{-}57)$$

In this reaction the adduct contains a new carbon-metal bond. However, the most general view of this reaction type would embrace all additions of metallic salts to olefin and acetylenes, even if there is no carbon-metal bond in the reactants. The adducts formed from mercuric salts[57] (Eq. 6–58), boron halides[58] (Eq. 6–59), dialkylaluminum halides[59] (Eq. 6–60), and other

$$RCH\!\!=\!\!CHR + Hg(OCOCH_3)_2 + CH_3OH \longrightarrow RCH\!\!-\!\!\!-\!\!CHR \qquad (6\text{-}58)$$
$$\underset{\displaystyle OCH_3}{|} \quad \underset{\displaystyle HgOCOCH_3}{|}$$

$$C_6H_5C\!\!\equiv\!\!CC_6H_5 + C_6H_5BBr_2 \rightleftharpoons C_6H_5C\!\!=\!\!CC_6H_5 \qquad (6\text{-}59)$$
$$\underset{\displaystyle \underset{\displaystyle Br}{\overset{\displaystyle |}{C_6H_5\!\!-\!\!B}}}{|} \quad \underset{\displaystyle Br}{|}$$

$$(C_2H_5)_2AlCl + CH_2 \xrightarrow{\ (CH_2N_2)\ } (C_2H_5)_2AlCH_2Cl \qquad (6\text{-}60)$$

metalloid halides, acetates, or related salts typify this general reaction. The reaction is readily reversible in many instances; indeed, the formation of carbenes by α-elimination and of arynes by α,β-elimination of metal halides

---

[57] J. Romeyn and G. F Wright, *J. Am. Chem. Soc.*, **69**, 697 (1947).
[58] (a) J. J. Eisch and L. J. Gonsior, unpublished studies, 1965; (b) cf. M. F. Lappert and B. Prokai, *J. Organometal. Chem.* (*Amsterdam*), **1**, 384 (1964).
[59] H. Hoberg, *Angew. Chem.*, **73**, 114 (1961); *Ann.*, **656**, 1 (1962).

are vivid examples (Eq. 6–33). Another noteworthy reversal is the smooth thermal elimination of alkene from β-haloalkylsilanes [60] (Eq. 6–61). One can expect interesting organometallic syntheses to emerge from further halometalation studies.

$$(C_2H_5)_2ClSi—CH_2CH_2—Cl \xrightarrow{AlCl_3} (C_2H_5)_2SiCl_2 + CH_2{=}CH_2\uparrow \qquad (6\text{–}61)$$

CARBOMETALATION

The addition of metal alkyls to unsaturated linkages is distinctly of narrower scope than either of the foregoing reactions. Not only is the possibility of reaction limited to alkyls of Groups IA–IIIA and the transition metals, but many side reactions intervene. In fact, prior to Ziegler's study of Group IIIA alkyls,[61] successful additions of organomagnesium [62] and organoalkali [63] compounds had been achieved only with conjugated olefins (Eq. 6–62). Such additions are intimately associated with the mechanism for the

$$(6\text{–}62)$$

anionic polymerization of diene and styrene monomers [64] (Eq. 6–63). In recent research alkali metal alkyls have been found to add to α-olefins under more drastic conditions and even Grignard reagents finally have been shown to add to certain types of unconjugated C=C linkages [65]:

$$(6\text{–}63)$$

$$(6\text{–}64)$$

[60] L. H. Sommer et al., *J. Am. Chem. Soc.*, **70**, 2869 (1948).

[61] K. Ziegler, *Experientia Suppl.*, **1955**, 274.

[62] M. S. Kharasch and O. Reinmuth, *Grignard Reactions of Nonmetallic Substances*, Prentice-Hall, Englewood Cliffs, N.J., 1954, p. 87.

[63] K. Ziegler and K. Bähr, *Ber.*, **61**, 253 (1928).

[64] Cf., *inter alia*, M. Shima et al., *J. Am. Chem. Soc.*, **85**, 1306 (1963).

[65] J. J. Eisch and G. R. Husk, *J. Am. Chem. Soc.*, **87**, 4194 (1965).

The choice of solvent should be governed by the metal alkyl being added, for the use of a donor medium can promote or retard the rate of adduction. Sodium and higher alkali metal alkyls are destroyed rapidly in ether media, while aluminum alkyls form stable etherates which are far less reactive toward alkenes.[66] Similarly, the preparation of substituted vinylaluminum compounds by the interaction of alkynes with triphenylaluminum (Eq. 6–65) is halted by cineole.[67] Between these extremes, as for example with lithium alkyls, ether accelerates the rate of adduction over that for hydrocarbon solution.[68]

$$C_6H_5C{\equiv}CC_6H_5 + (C_6H_5)_3Al \rightarrow \underset{C_6H_5}{\overset{C_6H_5}{\diagup}}C{=}C\underset{Al(C_6H_5)_2}{\overset{C_6H_5}{\diagup}} \tag{6–65}$$

Among the many side reactions which interfere with the preparative intent of this reaction are those of concurrent metalation, isomerization and polymerization. The latter process becomes especially important with transition metal alkyls and even with sluggish reactions of the main group metal alkyls. In addition, many of the difficulties encountered with hydrometalation crop up here because of thermal reactions involving olefin and metal hydride (Eqs. 6–54 to 6–56).

Carbanions as Ligands in Complexes

Adduction between metal alkyls or salts with other organometallics or alkyl halides leads to an increase in coordination number for the metal M' (Eq. 6 66). This method provides a general route either to organometallic

$$M'Y + MZ \rightleftharpoons M^+(Y{-}M'{-}Z)^- \tag{6–66}$$

σ-complexes or to mixed metal alkyls of higher valence. Note that the adduction is reversible, where the reverse process corresponds to dissociation or reduction.[69] Moreover, the adducts given below illustrate the genetic relationship between organoidal-metallic and organometallic compounds:

$$C_6H_5Na + C_6H_5Li \rightleftharpoons Na[Li(C_6H_5)_2] \tag{6–67[70]}$$

$$CH_3CH_2Li + (CH_3CH_2)_3Al \rightarrow Li[Al(CH_2CH_3)_4] \tag{6–68[71]}$$

$$C_6H_5Li + (C_6H_5)_2Sn \rightarrow (C_6H_5)_3SnLi \tag{6–69[72]}$$

[66] K. Ziegler and W.-R. Kroll, *Ann.*, **629**, 167 (1960).
[67] J. J. Eisch and C. K. Hordis, unpublished studies, 1966.
[68] K. Ziegler and W. Schäfer, *Ann.*, **511**, 101 (1934).
[69] Cf. F. R. Jensen and R. J. Ouellette, *J. Am. Chem. Soc.*, **85**, 363 (1963), for examples of reduction in the solvolysis of alkylmercury salts.
[70] G. Wittig, *Angew. Chem.*, **70**, 65 (1958).
[71] (a) E. B. Baker and H. H. Sisler, *J. Am. Chem. Soc.*, **75**, 5193 (1953); (b) K. Ziegler, H.-G. Gellert, H. Martin, K. Nagel, and J. Schneider, *Ann.*, **589**, 91 (1954).
[72] G. Wittig, F. J. Meyer, and G. Lange, *Ann.*, **571**, 169, 193 (19)51.

$$RLi + R_4Ti \rightarrow R_5TiLi \qquad (6\text{–}70)^{73}$$

$$CH_3I + GeI_2 \rightarrow CH_3GeI_3 \qquad (6\text{–}71)^{74}$$

The limitation of this method lies in requiring the organometallic acceptor component to be in a lower oxidation state or to possess a pronounced Lewis acidity. In the case of an alkyl of a metal in a lower valence state, the resultant product is an organoidal-metallic compound. The fact that such adducts may dissociate into its components, that different organic groups may be exchanged in the process and that competing metal-hydrogen and metal-halogen exchanges may occur further curtails successful applications of the method.

Elimination

As each of the foregoing adductions is reversible in principle, this thermal elimination may be utilized to prepare alkylmetal halides and hydrides. Practicality requires that the starting metal alkyl be accessible by an independent route (Eqs. 6–72 and 6–73). In other situations, these thermal eliminations are important in organometallic reaction mechanisms (Eq. 6–74).

$$(CH_3CHCH_2)_3Al \underset{\Delta}{\rightleftharpoons} (CH_3CHCH_2)_2AlH + (CH_3)_2C{=}CH_2 \qquad (6\text{–}72)^{75}$$
$$\quad\ |\qquad\qquad\qquad\qquad\quad\ |$$
$$\quad CH_3\qquad\qquad\qquad\qquad CH_3$$

$$(CH_3CH)_2Be \xrightarrow{\Delta} [CH_3CHBeH]_x + CH_3CH{=}CH_2 \qquad (6\text{–}73)^{76}$$
$$\qquad |$$
$$\quad CH_3$$

$$\overset{O}{\underset{}{\overset{\|}{(C_6H_5)_3C{-}C{-}C_6H_5}}} \xrightarrow{C_6H_5Li} [(C_6H_5)_3C{-}\overset{Li^{\oplus}O^{\ominus}}{\underset{}{\overset{|}{C}}}(C_6H_5)_2] \xrightarrow{C_6H_5Li}$$

$$(C_6H_5)_3CLi + (C_6H_5)_3COLi \qquad (6\text{–}74)^{77a}$$

Finally, dehalometalation is fundamental to the efficacy of novel carbene or carbenoid precursors based on α-haloalkyl derivatives of zinc[77b] or of mercury[77c]:

$$(6\text{–}74a)$$

[73] L. Summers, R. H. Uloth, and A. Holmes, *J. Am. Chem. Soc.*, **77**, 3604 (1955).
[74] L. F. Audrieth (ed.), *Inorganic Synthesis*, Vol. III, McGraw-Hill, New York, 1950, p. 64.
[75] K. Ziegler et al., *Ann.*, **629**, 1 (1960).
[76] G. E. Coates and F. Glockling, *J. Chem. Soc.*, *1954*, 2526.
[77] (a) J. J. Eisch, unpublished studies, 1962; (b) H. E. Simmons and R. D. Smith, *J. Am. Chem. Soc.*, **81**, 4256 (1959); **86**, 1337, 1347 (1964); (c) D. Seyferth et al., *ibid.*, **87**, 4259 (1965).

Displacement

The interaction of the free metal with an organometallic can lead to a metal displacement. For a spontaneous reaction a more active metal is admixed with a mercury alkyl in a solvent-free or hydrocarbon medium. Amalgamation of the displaced metal contributes to the completion of the reaction:

$$(CH_3CH_2)_2Hg + xNa \rightarrow 2CH_3CH_2Na + Hg \cdot Na \qquad (6\text{--}75)^{[78]}$$

$$(C_6H_5)_2Hg + xAl \rightarrow (C_6H_5)_3Al + Hg \cdot Al \qquad (6\text{--}76)^{[79]}$$

To obtain a less reactive metal alkyl from a more reactive alkyl, energy must be introduced. This is the basis for the electrolytic preparation of certain alkyls such as those of lead:

$$4(CH_3CH_2)_3Al + 3Pb \xrightarrow{\text{electrol.}} 3(CH_3CH_2)_4Pb + 4Al \qquad (6\text{--}77)^{[80]}$$

The difficulty with the displacement synthesis is the necessity of starting with a pre-formed metal alkyl. Often such reagents are themselves difficult to prepare or are unstable to metal elimination under the reaction conditions. Furthermore, isomerization of the alkyl group and an incomplete metal exchange may make purification unfeasible. On the other hand, this reaction is the most important general synthesis of pure metal alkyls, since contamination with donor solvents and metal salts is avoided.

A somewhat related reaction, namely, the reaction of free radicals themselves or their precursors with free metals, can lead to metal alkyls in certain cases. The decomposition of aryldiazonium compounds in the presence of metal salts and the scavenging of thermally generated alkyl radicals by metal mirrors (Paneth technique) illustrate such reactions:

$$C_6H_5\overset{+}{N}\equiv N \ Cl^- \xrightarrow{HgCl_2} C_6H_5HgCl \qquad (6\text{--}78)^{[81]}$$

$$(C_2H_5)_4Pb \xrightarrow{\varDelta} Pb + 4C_2H_5 \xrightarrow{Te} (C_2H_5)_2Te \qquad (6\text{--}79)^{[82]}$$

$$2(C_6H_5)_3C + Mg + MgI_2 \longrightarrow 2(C_6H_5)_3CMgI \qquad (6\text{--}80)^{[83]}$$

Rearrangements

The isomerization of an organometallic compound can be disconcerting when encountered for the first time. Thereafter, the rearrangement can be

[78] W. Schlenk and J. Holtz, *Ber.*, **50**, 262 (1917).
[79] (a) H. Gilman and K. E. Marple, *Rec. trav. chim.*, **55**, 135 (1936); (b) W. C. Kaska, doctoral dissertation, University of Michigan, Ann Arbor, 1963.
[80] K. Ziegler and H. Lehmkuhl, *Angew. Chem.*, **67**, 424 (1955).
[81] A. N. Nesmeyanov, *Ber.*, **62**, 1010, 1018 (1929).
[82] F. A. Paneth and W. Hofeditz, *Ber.*, **62**, 1335 (1929).
[83] M. Gomberg and W. E. Bachmann, *J. Am. Chem. Soc.*, **52**, 2455 (1930).

turned to preparative advantage, if the rate and equilibrium favor the complete formation of the rearranged product. In general, the site of the new carbon-metal bond will be preferred in the usual sequence of carbanionic stabilities: acetylenic > allylic > vinyl ~ phenyl > primary alkyl > secondary alkyl > tertiary alkyl. Donor solvents (tetrahydrofuran), Lewis acids (AlCl$_3$), or transition metal salts (TiCl$_4$) can accelerate the rate of such rearrangements. A cross section of representative processes is indicated below:

$$[(CH_3)_3C]_3B \longrightarrow [(CH_3)_2CHCH_2]_3B \qquad (6\text{–}81)[84]$$

$$\triangleright\!\!-\!CH_2Li \longrightarrow CH_2\!=\!CHCH_2CH_2Li \qquad (6\text{–}82)[85]$$

$$(C_6H_5)_3CCH_2K \longrightarrow (C_6H_5)_2CKCH_2C_6H_5 \qquad (6\text{–}83)[86]$$

$$\underset{R}{\overset{C_6H_5}{>}}C\!=\!C\underset{Li}{\overset{C_6H_5}{<}} \xrightarrow{\text{ether}} \underset{R}{\overset{C_6H_5}{>}}C\!=\!C\underset{C_6H_5}{\overset{Li}{<}} \qquad (6\text{–}84)[87]$$

$$(6\text{–}85)[88]$$

In all these interconversion methods for organometallic compounds the prime consideration is to obtain the new metal alkyl in high yield and free of isomeric products. It may not be necessary to isolate certain reactive metal alkyl intermediates (Grignard and organolithium reagents) in the pure state; preparation in solution often suffices. However, the ultimate goal usually is the synthesis of pure organometallic compounds for further physicochemical investigation. This requires not only elaborate procedures for the purification of the metal alkyl products, but also a reliable determination of the structure and the purity of the final product. In contrast with this, Chapter Seven discusses the role of organometallic reagents in synthesizing metal-free organic compounds. Although some precautions are required to prevent the undesired consumption of the organometallic reagent by air and moisture, the over-all experimental technique is considerably simpler.

[84] G. F. Hennion, P. A. McCusker, E. C. Ashby, and A. J. Rutkowski, *J. Am. Chem. Soc.*, **79**, 5190 (1957).

[85] P. T. Lansbury, V. A. Pattison, W. A. Clement, and J. D. Sidler, *J. Am. Chem. Soc.*, **86**, 2247 (1965).

[86] E. Grovenstein and L. P. Williams, *J. Am. Chem. Soc.*, **83**, 412 (1961).

[87] D. Y. Curtin and W. J. Koehl, *J. Am. Chem. Soc.*, **84**, 1967 (1962).

[88] (a) H. Gilman and H. A. Pacevitz, *J. Am. Chem. Soc.*, **62**, 673 (1940); (b) H. Gilman, H. A. Pacevitz, and O. Baine, *ibid.*, **62**, 1514 (1940).

SEVEN

Organometallic Reagents in Organic Synthesis

General Aspects of Synthetic Scope

CURRENT PROSPECTS

Once the recluse of academic research laboratories who ventured only seldom into the world of chemical industry, organometallic compounds now are recognized as one of the most significant areas of industrial organic chemistry. Before the early 1950s, the toxicity, flammability, explosive hydrolysis, and general cost of organometallic reagents had been viewed as decisive reasons for leaving organometallic chemistry to the academicians. However, the concurrent development of organometallic π-complexes of transition metals and the exciting hydrocarbon chemistry of Group IIIA metal alkyls and hydrides in the 1950s changed industry's mind abruptly. In fact, the subsequent stormy efforts of industrial research groups to exploit promising avenues of organometallic research had the flavor of a gold rush. The search for the rainbow happily has now disappeared, but a high level of realistic interest in organometallic reagents continues. The legacy of this heightened research activity is the discovery of many novel organic synthetic methods utilizing organometallic reagents. In turn, this demand for certain metal alkyls has prompted their commercial preparation for purchase by interested researchers. The commercial availability of the alkyls of lithium, magnesium, boron, aluminum, and tin, *inter alia*, has added greatly to the

117

convenience of their use.[1] Moreover, the common accessibility of apparatus for manipulating air-sensitive reagents has decreased significantly the hazards of working with these chemicals. Present research trends suggest that an increasing amount of organic synthesis will involve organometallic reagents because of their unique and selective reactions.

SYNTHETIC SUITABILITY OF PARTICULAR METAL ALKYLS

Viewed by the synthetic organic chemist, the choice of a given metal alkyl is governed by its ability to undergo a desired reaction with speed and selectivity. The factor of reaction rate by itself prompts one to use the highly ionic alkali metal members. The polar addition and substitution reactions discussed in Chapter Four all take place with maximum rapidity with these metal alkyls. However, the second factor of selectivity is often of greater importance. The types of addition that occur with unsaturated substrates (for example, 1,2- versus 1,4-addition), or competitive reactions between different groups, *e.g.*, ester and keto carbonyls,

$$\underset{\text{R---C---CH}_2\text{CH}_2\text{---C---OR}'}{\overset{\overset{\displaystyle O}{\|}\qquad\qquad\overset{\displaystyle O}{\|}}{}}$$

can result in isomeric products with indiscriminating organometallic reagents. Moreover, competition between addition and substitution processes may be serious, either because the metal alkyl is too reactive (RK) or because it is too unreactive (RMgX). The tendency of potassium alkyls to abstract protons from most organic compounds would overshadow many carbonyl addition processes. The lessened reactivity of Grignard reagents to addition permits enolate salt formation to win out[2,3]:

$$\underset{\overset{\displaystyle |}{\underset{\displaystyle R}{\text{C}_6\text{H}_5\text{---C---N}}}\overset{\overset{\displaystyle R'\text{CH}_2}{\displaystyle |}}{}\diagdown\overset{\displaystyle C_6\text{H}_5}{\diagup}\underset{\displaystyle \text{Li}}{}}{} \xleftarrow{\text{RLi}[2]} \underset{\overset{\displaystyle C_6\text{H}_5}{\diagup}}{\overset{\displaystyle R'\text{CH}_2}{\diagdown}}\text{C}=\text{N}\overset{\displaystyle C_6\text{H}_5}{\diagup} \xrightarrow{\text{RMgX}[3]} \underset{\overset{\displaystyle C_6\text{H}_5}{\diagup}}{\overset{\displaystyle R'\text{CH}}{\diagdown}}\text{C---N}\overset{\displaystyle C_6\text{H}_5}{\underset{\displaystyle \text{MgX}}{\diagdown}} \qquad (7\text{--}1)$$

Then too, especially with substitution by metal alkyls, the kind and site of substitution makes the selectivity factor of prime importance. The isomeric metalation products obtained from cumene and *n*-amylpotassium (Eq. 6–28)

---

[1] Cf. *inter alia*, the chemicals offered by the American firms: Alpha, Arapahoe, Callery, Foote, M & T, Metallomer, Orgmet, Pressare, Stauffer, and Strem.
[2] H. Gilman and J. Eisch, *J. Am. Chem. Soc.*, **79**, 2150 (1957).
[3] G. Plancher and C. Ravenna, *Atti Accad. Lincei*, *14* [5], 555 (1906); *Chem. Zentr.*, **1**, 111 (1907).

emphasize the desirability of selective metalating agents. Finally, the stereo-selectivity of a specific organometallic reaction (retention or inversion of configuration and *cis* or *trans* addition) may favor the use of a specific metal alkyl in organic synthesis.

A brief survey of the organic synthetic applications for individual metal alkyls now seems in order. In Group IA, lithium alkyls strike an excellent balance between reactivity and selectivity. Whereas the alkyls of sodium and potassium are potent metalating agents for hydrocarbons of low acidity,[4] lithium alkyls (*n*-butyl and phenyl) are selective in effecting monometalation adjacent to an electronegative group. This can be achieved by metal-hydrogen or metal-halogen exchange. Compared with Grignard reagents, lithium alkyls can add more readily to C=E linkages and, in fact, can add to linkages to which magnesium alkyls are essentially inert: C=C—C=C, C=N of pyridine and carboxylate salts. When a potent base is sought for diverse reactions (benzyne or carbenoid processes or base-catalyzed rearrangements), organo-lithium reagents are frequent choices. This pronounced nucleophilicity toward protons carries over to other positive centers. Thus one finds that lithium alkyls are the most useful alkylating agents for metalloid salts:

$$C_6H_5ICl_2 + 2C_6H_5Li \xrightarrow{-80°} (C_6H_5)_3I + 2LiCl \qquad (7\text{-}2)^5$$

In Group IIA the organometallics of magnesium and calcium presently are the only members of synthetic interest. To extol the virtues of magnesium is superfluous; others have done this well and copiously.[6] Two features of Grignard reagent behavior of specific value are the occurrence of conjugate addition with α,β-unsaturated systems (C=C—C=E)[6] (Eq. 7-3) and the tendency for rearrangement with allylic systems[7] (Eq. 7-4):

$$\underset{\underset{H}{|}}{\overset{\overset{H}{|}}{C_6H_5C}}=C-\overset{\overset{O}{\|}}{C}-C_6H_5$$

$$\xrightarrow[\text{2. } H_2O]{\text{1. } C_6H_5MgBr} (C_6H_5)_2CHCH_2-\overset{\overset{O}{\|}}{C}-C_6H_5 + \underset{\underset{H}{|}}{\overset{\overset{H}{|}}{C_6H_5C}}=C-\overset{\overset{OH}{|}}{C}(C_6H_5)_2 \qquad (7\text{-}3)$$

$$85\% \qquad\qquad\qquad 3\%$$

[4] R. A. Benkeser, D. J. Foster, D. M. Sauve, and J. F. Nobis, *Chem. Rev.*, **57**, 867 (1957).

[5] G. Wittig, *Angew. Chem.*, **70**, 65 (1958).

[6] M. S. Kharasch and O. Reinmuth, *Grignard Reactions of Nonmetallic Substances*, Prentice-Hall, Englewood Cliffs, N.J., 1954.

[7] H. Gilman and R. H. Kirby, *J. Am. Chem. Soc.*, **63**, 2046 (1941).

$$\text{(7-4)}^{8}$$

One fruitful area of Grignard chemistry is that of transition metal additives. First scouted by Kharasch and co-workers,[6] these reactions have interesting preparative possibilities. The ability of small amounts of transition metal salts to favor 1,4- over 1,2-addition,[9] to promote bimolecular reduction over 1,2-carbonyl addition[6] or to isomerize alkyl groups in $RMgX$,[10] is fascinating, but only partly understood. In contrast to magnesium, the organometallic chemistry of the common metal, calcium, has received little attention. The greater reactivity of calcium alkyls in metalation and addition reactions (Eq. 7–5) is reminiscent of lithium alkyls and valuable synthetic applications can be expected to result eventually.[14]

$$\text{(7-5)}^{11, 12, 13}$$

The greatest synthetic value of Group IIIA alkyls and hydrides lies in the area of hydrocarbon chemistry, especially in the preparation and reactions of simple alkenes and alkynes.

The greater ease of adding B—H bonds to carbon-carbon unsaturation makes boron hydrides the reagents of choice in modifying functional groups on a given carbon skeleton. In a complementary fashion, aluminum alkyls are most important in changing the size of the carbon skeleton, since Al—C, but

[8] M. Tiffeneau and R. Delange, *J. Chem. Soc.*, **86**, 48 (1904).

[9] A. J. Birch and M. Smith, *Proc. Chem. Soc.*, **1962**, 356.

[10] H. L. Finkbeiner and G. D. Cooper, *J. Org. Chem.*, **26**, 4779 (1961).

[11] (a) H. Gilman and R. V. Young, *J. Am. Chem. Soc.*, **56**, 1415 (1934); (b) H. Gilman and R. L. Bebb, *ibid.*, **61**, 109 (1939).

[12] H. Gilman, R. H. Kirby, M. Lichtenwalter, and R. V. Young, *Rec. trav. chim.*, **55**, 79 (1936).

[13] (a) H. Gilman and D. L. Esmay, *J. Am. Chem. Soc.*, **76**, 5786 (1954); (b) H. Gilman, A. L. Jacoby, and H. A. Pacevitz, *J. Org. Chem.*, **3**, 120 (1938).

[14] D. Bryce-Smith and A. C. Skinner, *Chem. Ind.* (*London*), **1960**, 1106.

usually not B—C, bonds add to C=C and C≡C linkages. As to the stoichiometry of the R_3M chemistry (R = alkyl or hydrogen), however, it should be noted that often all three bonds are not available for fruitful reaction. For either steric (Eq. 7–6) or electronic reasons (Eq. 7–7) a given reaction may stop after one or two M—H or M—C bonds have responded. Also significant is the catalytic action of these metal hydrides in isomerizing and dimerizing unsaturated hydrocarbons.

$$4(CH_3)_2C{=}C(CH_3)H + B_2H_6 \rightarrow \left[\underset{\underset{CH_3}{|}}{(CH_3)_2CHCH} \right]_2 BH \qquad (7{-}6)^{15}$$

$$(C_2H_5)_3Al + H{-}C{\equiv}C{-}H \rightarrow (C_2H_5)_2Al{-}\overset{H}{C}{=}\overset{H}{C}{-}C_6H_5 \qquad (7{-}7)^{16}$$

In compounds of the other main group metalloids (IVA–VIIA), a few specific organic synthetic applications have been reported. Halomethyl derivatives of Group IVA have some potential as carbene precursors;[17] alkyltin hydrides can reduce alkyl halides to alkanes smoothly;[18] and lead(IV) acetate oxidations may involve organolead intermediates in some instances.[19] The alkylphosphonium and related Group VA derivatives have found use as ylide precursors in the Wittig reaction[20] and phenyliodonium compounds have served as potential sources of "cationic" phenyl in many reactions.[21]

Members of Group IIB have been employed in cases (a) where Grignard reagents are too reactive, as in the preparation of ketones from acid chlorides and cadmium alkyls;[22] (b) where specific alkylations are required, as in preparing alkanes with quaternary carbons from *tert*-alkyl halides and zinc alkyls:

$$R'{-}\underset{\underset{R''}{|}}{\overset{\overset{R}{|}}{C}}{-}Cl + R_2'''Zn \rightarrow R'{-}\underset{\underset{R''}{|}}{\overset{\overset{R}{|}}{C}}{-}R'' + R'''{-}Zn{-}Cl \qquad (7{-}8)^{23}$$

[15] H. C. Brown and B. C. Subba Rao, *J. Am. Chem. Soc.*, **81**, 6428 (1959).
[16] G. Wilke and H. Müller, *Ann.*, **629**, 222 (1960).
[17] H. C. Clark and C. J. Willis, *J. Am. Chem. Soc.*, **82**, 1888 (1960).
[18] L. A. Rothman and E. I. Becker, *J. Org. Chem.*, **25**, 2203 (1960).
[19] R. Criegee, *Angew. Chem.*, **70**, 173 (1958).
[20] U. Schöllkopf, *Angew. Chem.*, **71**, 260 (1959).
[21] F. M. Beringer et al., *J. Am. Chem. Soc.*, **75**, 2705, 2708 (1953).
[22] D. A. Shirley in *Organic Reactions*, Vol. VIII (R. Adams, ed.), Wiley, New York, 1954, Chap. 2.
[23] C. R. Noller, *J. Am. Chem. Soc.*, **51**, 594 (1929).

and (c) where electrophilic metalation of aromatic rings provides a path to substituents, as in mercuration:

$$(7-9)^{24}$$

Although the Reformatsky reaction (action of zinc and an α-haloester on a ketone) formally resembles a Grignard synthesis, the intermediate zinc compound may well be an enolate salt, $CH_2{=}COZnX(OR)$, rather than an organozinc system.

No simple summary can be made of the synthetic applications of transition metal organometallics. Here the catalytic importance of σ and π metal alkyls surpasses their stoichiometric applications. Apparently successful catalytic behavior and the thermal stability of an alkyl seem to be inversely related in many cases. Thus, with just those metals whose alkyls are difficult to isolate (first transition series), catalytic activity in various olefin reactions is optimal: reduction (Ni), hydrocarbonylation (Co), oligomerization (Ni), and polymerization (Ti, Cr).

Organometallic Intermediates and Experimental Conditions

In organic synthetic applications not only does one employ an organometallic starting material (I) but often a metastable organometallic intermediate (II) is produced. Subsequent chemical treatment leads to the desired metal-free product (III; for example, Eqs. 7–9 and 7–10).

$$R-M \xrightarrow[\text{step 1}]{H_2C{=}CH_2} R-CH_2CH_2M \xrightarrow[\text{2. }H_2O]{\text{1. (O)}} R-CH_2CH_2OH \qquad (7\text{-}10)$$

$$\text{step 2}$$

I II III

Naturally the starting material RM (I) must be protected from adventitious oxidation and hydrolysis. Dry, inert solvents and gas atmosphere are required, as mentioned above. For short reaction periods adequate protection may be provided by the vapor blanket arising from volatile solvents (pentane, ethyl ether), especially if small amounts of oxidation are permissible (many

[24] F. C. Whitmore and E. R. Hanson, *Organic Syntheses*, 2nd ed., Vol. I, Wiley, New York, 1941, pp. 161, 326.

Grignard reactions). Also many ethers (THF and glycol ethers) and tertiary amines, which are excellent promoters for organometallic reactions, can be used, even though they are attacked slowly by metal alkyls. However, the experimental conditions can also have a most decisive effect on the rate of formation and equilibrium concentration of the organometallic intermediate II. The factors deciding the speed of such individual reactions (metalations, additions) have been discussed in Chapter Six. Of special interest in this section are the ways in which the intermediate metal alkyl II can be destroyed or be isomerized into a new R′M. For these competing reactions will determine the feasibility of preparing III by the proposed method.

Whenever more than one intermediate RM compound (II) can be formed, kinetic and thermodynamic factors can control the nature of the principal RM product. The fastest formed product may rearrange to a more stable isomer (cf. Eqs. 6–81 to 6–85). Alternatively, the initially formed organometallic may react with itself, with the solvent, or with the original R—M (I) to form a new RM or to be destroyed. To an experimentalist, this suggests that a study of the final organic product (Eq. 7–10, III) as a function of reaction temperature and time may be most valuable. The resulting data may not only permit the isolation of optimal yields of a desired product, but also may reveal novel

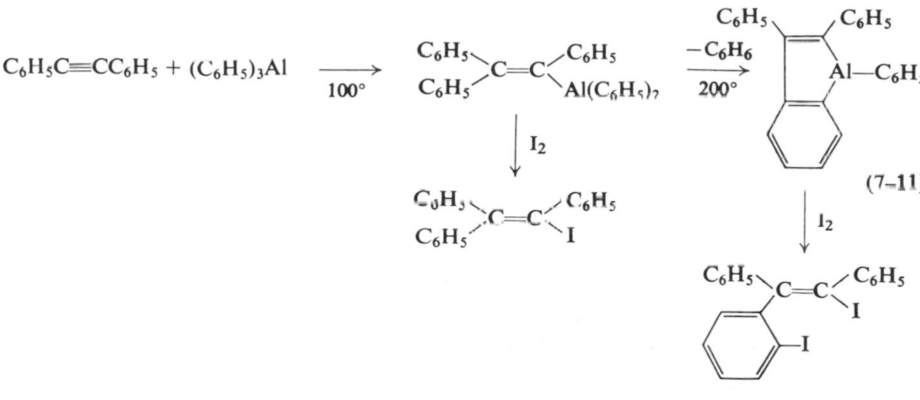

(7–11)

preparative routes[25] (Eq. 7–11). In particular cases, the organometallic intermediate II may prove to be too labile to persist until the final chemical treatment (step 2 in Eq. 7–10). In such situations the intermediate II can be

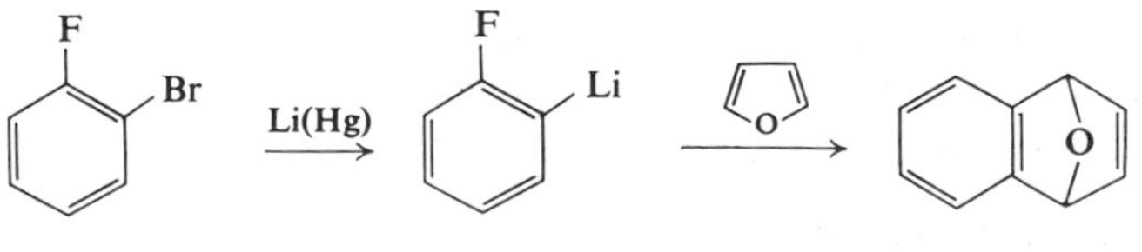

(7–12)

[25] (a) J. J. Eisch and W. C. Kaska, *J. Am. Chem. Soc.*, **84**, 1501 (1962); (b) J. J. Eisch and C. K. Hordis, unpublished studies, 1966.

prepared at lower temperatures in the presence of the chemical as a trapping agent. This technique has proved most useful in aryne and carbene reactions [26] (Eq. 7–12). Another instance of labile, reactive organometallics being generated and utilized *in situ* is the catalytic oligomerization and polymerization of alkenes by a combination of metal alkyl and transition metal salts (Ziegler-Natta catalysts).

Under certain experimental conditions an organometallic reagent may display a distinctly lower order of desired reactivity. At the same time another mode of reaction may be evident. It has been mentioned that rates of lithium-hydrogen exchanges by *n*-butyllithium are accelerated by a THF medium over those in ethyl ether. The converse is that such alkyls show a lower reactivity in hydrocarbons or in the presence of lithium halides.[27] In fact, an interesting reduction reaction takes precedence in hexane solution [28] (Eq. 7–13). In the

$$CH_3(CH_2)_6CH_2Br + CH_3CH_2CH_2CH_2Li \rightarrow CH_3(CH_2)_6CH_3 + CH_3CH_2CH{=}CH_2 + LiBr$$
$$(7\text{--}13)$$

latter medium, the associated species $[(RLi)_n$ and $(RLi \cdot LiX)_n]$ apparently can undergo other reactions more readily than metal-hydrogen or metal-halogen exchanges (cf. the behavior of dialkylaluminum hydrides toward alkynes, with or without the presence of R_3N as in Eq. 6–53). These findings stress the value of investigating the effect of solvent and of corresponding metal salt on the rate and mode of organometallic reactions.

Rearrangements in Organometallic Reactions

Not only can organometallic compounds isomerize to yield different alkyls, as discussed above, but their carbon-metal bonds can be ruptured with the formation of isomeric metal-free products. For preparative purposes it is not necessary to know whether the final product has the same configuration or a different configuration than that of the organometallic precursor. The structure of the organic product can be determined separately. However, one is most interested in the stereoselectivity of the reaction. Thus, when one can encounter position isomers (allylic products), geometrical isomers (*cis-trans* products), or optical isomers (retention or inversion of configuration), the organometallic reaction becomes most attractive when one product predominates. This outcome obtains for many carbon-metal bond cleavages (Chapter Five). In order to ascertain whether the reaction actually takes place with or without rearrangement, the structure of the metal alkyl must be

[26] G. Wittig and L. Pohmer, *Ber.*, **89**, 1334 (1956).
[27] W. Glaze and R. West, *J. Am. Chem. Soc.*, **82**, 4437 (1960).
[28] J. F. Eastham and G. W. Gibson, *J. Org. Chem.*, **28**, 280 (1963).

examined by a physical method. Nuclear magnetic resonance spectroscopy can be most helpful in reaching a decision on structure. Even the situation of a dynamic equilibrium between isomeric metal alkyls can be recognized by temperature-dependence studies of n.m.r. spectra.[29] In Eqs. 7–14 and 7–15 the results of physical and chemical studies are combined to reveal the occurrence of rearrangement (Eq. 7–14) or retention of structure (Eq. 7–15) in allylic systems:

$$CH_3CH{=}CHCH_2MgBr + CH_3{-}\underset{CH_3}{\overset{CH_3}{\diamondsuit}}{-}\overset{O}{\overset{\|}{C}}{-}CH_3 \longrightarrow$$

$$(7{-}14)\,^{30}$$

$$\underset{C_6H_5}{\overset{C_6H_5}{>}}\underset{\underset{AlR_2}{|}}{C}{-}\overset{H}{\underset{H}{C{=}C}}{-}CH_3 + D_2O \longrightarrow \underset{C_6H_5}{\overset{C_6H_5}{>}}\underset{\underset{D}{|}}{C}{-}\overset{H}{\underset{H}{C{=}C}}{-}CH_3$$

$$(7{-}15)\,^{31}$$

Preparation of Individual Classes of Organic Compounds

In the rapidly expanding field of synthesis by means of organometallic reagents, novel preparative methods are emerging continually. The succeeding discussion of introducing functional groups delineates only the present known scope of preparative routes. The ingenuity of the organic chemist undoubtedly will uncover new possibilities in functionally selective and stereospecific syntheses.

Hydrocarbons

It is precisely upon this type of compound that recent synthetic developments have had the greatest impact. The wide application of Group III metal alkyls and hydrides has made the chemical transformations of hydrocarbons a routine laboratory operation. These valuable synthetic methods include (a) the oligomerization and polymerization of olefins, acetylenes, and dienes

[29] J. E. Nordlander and J. D. Roberts, *J. Am. Chem. Soc.*, **81**, 1769 (1959).
[30] J. E. Nordlander, W. G. Young, and J. D. Roberts, *J. Am. Chem. Soc.*, **83**, 494 (1961).
[31] J. J. Eisch and G. R. Husk, *J. Organometal. Chem. (Amsterdam)*, **4**, 415 (1965).

(Eqs. 7–16 to 7–19); (b) the stereospecific *cis*-reduction of cycloolefins and acetylenes, permitting the preparation of specifically deuterated compounds (Eq. 7–20); and (c) the direct alkylation and arylation of carbon-carbon unsaturation (Eqs. 7–21 and 7–22):

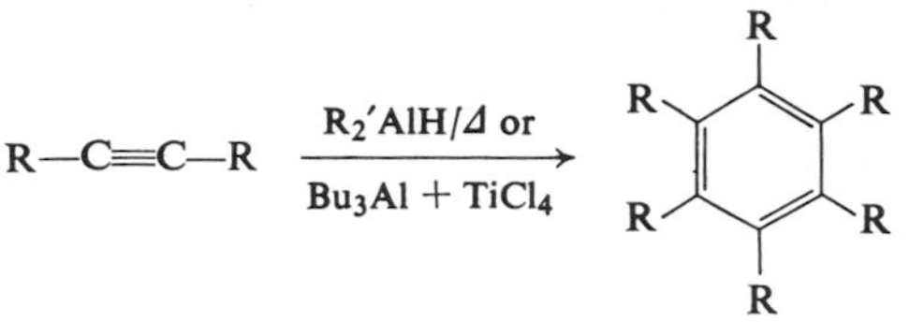

$$R-C\equiv C-R \xrightarrow[\text{Bu}_3\text{Al} + \text{TiCl}_4]{R_2'\text{AlH}/\Delta \text{ or}} \qquad (7\text{–}16)^{32}$$

$$X-(CH_2CH_2)_x-Y \xleftarrow[\text{TiCl}_4]{CH_2=CH_2} (CH_3CH_2)_3Al \xrightarrow[\text{Ni/C}_6\text{H}_5\text{C}\equiv\text{CH}]{CH_2=CH_2} CH_3CH_2CH=CH_2$$

$$(7\text{–}17)^{33, 34}$$

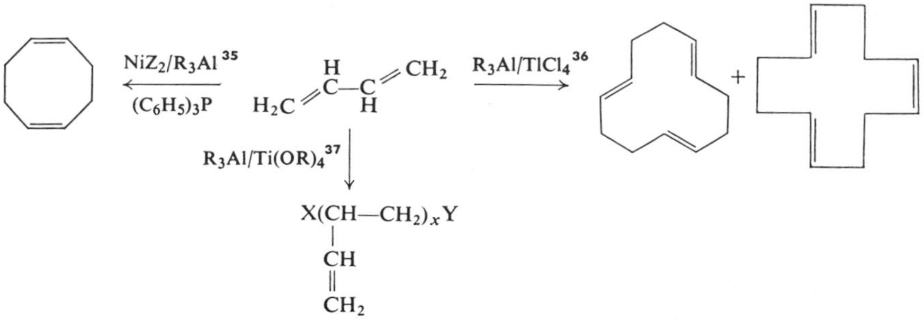

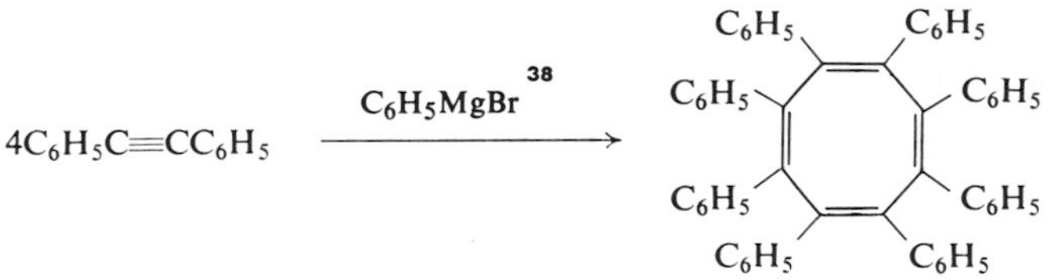

$$\xleftarrow[\text{(C}_6\text{H}_5)_3\text{P}]{\text{NiZ}_2/\text{R}_3\text{Al}^{35}} \quad \overset{H}{\underset{H_2C}{\diagup}}C-C\overset{CH_2}{\underset{H}{\diagdown}} \xrightarrow{\text{R}_3\text{Al}/\text{TlCl}_4{}^{36}} \qquad +$$

$$\Big\downarrow \text{R}_3\text{Al}/\text{Ti(OR)}_4{}^{37}$$

$$X(CH-CH_2)_xY$$
$$|$$
$$CH$$
$$\|$$
$$CH_2$$

$$4C_6H_5C\equiv CC_6H_5 \xrightarrow{C_6H_5MgBr \quad {}^{38}} \qquad (7\text{–}19)$$

32 (a) G. Wilke and H. Müller, *Ann.*, **629**, 222 (1960); (b) B. Franzus, P. J. Canterino, and R. A. Wickliffe, *J. Am. Chem. Soc.*, **81**, 1514 (1959).
33 K. Ziegler, E. Holzkamp, H. Breil, and H. Martin, *Angew. Chem.*, **67**, 426 (1955).
34 K. Ziegler, H.-G. Gellert, E. Holzkamp, G. Wilke, E. W. Duck, and W.-R. Kroll, *Ann.*, **629**, 172 (1960).
35 G. Wilke, *Angew. Chem.*, **75**, 10 (1963).
36 H. Breil, P. Heimbach, M. Kroner, H. Müller, and G. Wilke, *Makromolekul. Chem.*, **69**, 18 (1963).
37 G. Wilke, *Angew. Chem.*, **68**, 306 (1956).
38 M. Tsutsui, *Chem. Ind. (London)*, 780 (1962).

$$
R-C\equiv C-H
\begin{array}{c}
\xrightarrow{R_2'AlH\,[39]} \\
\\
\xrightarrow{R_2'AlD\,[40]}
\end{array}
\begin{array}{c}
\underset{H}{\overset{R}{>}}C=C\underset{AlR_2'}{\overset{H}{<}} \xrightarrow{D_2O} \underset{H}{\overset{R}{>}}C=C\underset{D}{\overset{H}{<}} \\[2mm]
\underset{D}{\overset{R}{>}}C=C\underset{AlR_2'}{\overset{H}{<}} \xrightarrow{H_2O} \underset{D}{\overset{R}{>}}C=C\underset{H}{\overset{H}{<}}
\end{array}
\qquad (7\text{-}20)
$$

$$
\begin{array}{c}
CH_2-CH_2-CH_2 \\
| \qquad\qquad \diagdown \\
CH_2 \qquad\quad CH \\
\diagdown \qquad\quad \| \\
AlR_2 \qquad\quad CH_2
\end{array}
\longrightarrow
\underset{H^{\diagdown} \ CH_2AlR_2}{\square}
\xrightarrow{H_2O}
\underset{CH_3}{\square}
\qquad (7\text{-}21)^{[41]}
$$

$$
C_6H_5-C\equiv C-C_6H_5 \xrightarrow[\text{2. } H_2O]{\text{1. } (C_6H_5)_3Al}
\underset{\underset{H \ \ C_6H_5}{| \ \ |}}{C_6H_5-C=C-C_6H_5}
\qquad (7\text{-}22)^{[42]}
$$

Another rapidly unfolding aspect of synthesis is the organometallic route to unstable intermediates whose decomposition leads to hydrocarbons. Of especial interest is the generation of free radicals, carbenes, and benzynes (arynes). In many cases the actual existence of the salt-free species has not been demonstrated, and their existence is presumed on the basis of observed reactions, chiefly dimerization and addition. As to the practical generation of radicals, some oxidative treatment of organometallics is required.[43] In principle, this might be molecular oxygen, halogen, or azo compound (Eq. 7-23). In practice, transition metal salts are most feasible[44] (Eq. 7-24). Apparently unstable transition metal alkyls are formed and then decompose homolytically. It is ironical that the dependence upon the instability of

$$
CH_3-\!\!\bigcirc\!\!-MgX \xrightarrow{O_2} CH_3-\!\!\bigcirc\!\!-\!\!\bigcirc\!\!-CH_3 + CH_3-\!\!\bigcirc\!\!-OH \quad (7\text{-}23)^{[43]}
$$

$$
C_6H_5-C\equiv C-MgX \xrightarrow{Cu^{++}} C_6H_5-C\equiv C-C\equiv C-C_6H_5 \qquad (7\text{-}24)
$$

[39] G. Wilke and H. Müller, *Ber.*, **89**, 444 (1956).

[40] G. Wilke and H. Müller, *Ann.*, **618**, 267 (1958).

[41] K. Ziegler, *Angew. Chem.*, **68**, 721 (1956).

[42] J. J. Eisch and W. C. Kaska, *J. Am. Chem. Soc.*, **84**, 1501 (1962).

[43] (a) See reference 6, pp. 116–132; (b) cf. G. A. Russell, E. G. Jansen, and E. T. Strom, *J. Am. Chem. Soc.*, **86**, 1807 (1964), for the formation of radical-anion intermediates from carbanions by electron transfer to unsaturated organic acceptors; (c) E. Müller and T. Töpel, *Ber.*, **72B**, 273 (1939).

[44] (a) H. Gilman, R. G. Jones, and L. A. Woods, *J. Am. Chem. Soc.*, **76**, 3615 (1954); (b) H. C. Brown, C. Verbrugge, and C. H. Snyder, *ibid.*, **83**, 1001 (1961); (c) H. C. Brown, N. C. Hebert, and C. H. Snyder, *ibid.*, **83**, 1001 (1961); (d) H. C. Brown and C. H. Snyder, *ibid.*, **83**, 1002 (1961).

iron alkyls prompted a synthesis of bicyclopentadienyl from C_5H_5MgX and $FeCl_3$.[45] The serendipitous synthesis of ferrocene revealed dramatically how little transition metal-carbon bonding was really understood.[46]

Both the production of carbenes and of arynes involves the loss of metal halide from a geminal carbon atom or from vicinal positions on a ring. If the elimination of MX is not synchronous, then a simple organometallic reaction is at hand, rather than a carbene or benzyne process. This appears to be true in many so-called methylenation reactions involving M—CH₂—X. Of most appealing utility are the ensuing insertion and ring-generating additions:

$$(7\text{-}25)^{20}$$

$$(7\text{-}26)^{47}$$

$$(7\text{-}27)^{48,\ 49,\ 50}$$

$$(7\text{-}28)^{51}$$

One of the most versatile hydrocarbon syntheses involves the alkylation of organometallics by a suitable alkyl halide or related type:

$$R\text{—}M + R'\text{—}X \rightarrow R\text{—}R' + MX \qquad (7\text{-}29)$$

[45] T. J. Kealy and P. L. Pauson, *Nature*, **168**, 1039 (1951).
[46] Cf. M. Rosenblum, *Chemistry of the Iron Group Metallocenes: Ferrocene, Ruthenocene, and Osmocene*, Pt. 1, Wiley (Interscience), New York, 1966.
[47] G. L. Closs and L. E. Closs, *J. Am. Chem. Soc.*, **85**, 99 (1963).
[48] (a) H. E. Simmons and R. D. Smith, *J. Am. Chem. Soc.*, **80**, 5323 (1958); (b) D. Seyferth, J. M. Burlitch, R. J. Minasz, J. Y.-P. Mui, H. D. Simmons, A. J.-H. Treiber, and S. R. Dowd, *ibid.*, **87**, 4259 (1965).
[49] R. S. Shank and H. Shechter, *J. Org. Chem.*, **24**, 1825 (1959).
[50] G. Wittig and K. Schwarzenbach, *Ann.*, **650**, 1 (1962).
[51] G. Wittig and L. Pohmer, *Ber.*, **89**, 1334 (1956).

The method is feasible for a wide variety of metal alkyls, if account be taken of extremes in reactivity. Alkali metal alkyls (RK, RNa; less so, RLi) may provoke undesirable side reactions because of carbenes or arynes resulting from the metalation of RX. Then, too, the reaction may fail because of insufficient reactivity in RM (R_4Ge) or in RX (vinylic halides). In general, the yields of coupled hydrocarbon are highest when either component has allylic character. Some useful applications are the following:

$$C_6H_5MgBr + CH_2=CHCH_2Br \rightarrow C_6H_5CH_2CH=CH_2 + MgBr_2 \qquad (7\text{-}30)\,[52]$$

$$(C_6H_5)_3CLi + CH_3I \rightarrow (C_6H_5)_3CCH_3 + LiI \qquad (7\text{-}31)\,[53]$$

Finally, the most general hydrocarbon preparation to which all organometallic and organometalloidal compounds are heir is the cleavage of carbon-metal bonds by hydrogen sources. In the first place this could be accomplished by protolysis with active-hydrogen compounds (H—Z). Naturally its practicality dictates that the organometallic used be prepared from a different, more accessible organic type. The advantages of this approach have already been touched upon in many other contexts. The particular attraction in this method is the specific deuteration of hydrocarbons by D_2O which it permits (Eq. 7–20). In the second place, a carbon-hydrogen bond could be established by the hydrogenolysis of organometallics. In Chapter Five the preparation of metal hydrides by the hydrogenolysis of main group metal alkyls was mentioned. The practical use of hydrogen treatment of unsaturated compounds, of course, is catalytic hydrogenation. Recent studies point to an intimate connection between such well-known organic reductions and the hydrogenolysis of organometallics.[53a] The formation of π-complexes between olefins or acetylenes and unstable transition metal hydrides apparently sets the stage for σ-alkyl-metal bonding; subsequent hydrogenolysis completes the process and regenerates the catalyst (Eq. 7–32):

$$RCH=CH_2 \xrightarrow{\quad \geqslant M-H \quad} \geqslant M\cdots\!\!\begin{array}{c} RC \stackrel{H}{\diagdown} \\ CH_2 \\ H \end{array} \longrightarrow \geqslant M-CH_2CH_2R \xrightarrow{\quad H_2 \quad} RCH_2CH_2$$
$$+$$
$$\geqslant M-H$$
$$(7\text{-}32)$$

[52] E. B. Hershberg, *Helv. Chim. Acta*, **17**, 352 (1934).
[53] W. Schlenk and R. Ochs, *Ber.*, **49**, 608 (1916).
[53a] Cf., *inter alia*, the work of L. Vaska and R. E. Rhodes, *J. Am. Chem. Soc.*, **87**, 4970 (1965), on the homogeneous hydrogenation of olefins by well-defined complexes of iridium hydride.

Halides

Inasmuch as metal alkyls are often prepared from alkyl halides, the cleavage of C—M bonds by a halogen source to yield halides might seem to be only a diverting cycle of reactions. However, the method may be useful for halogen exchange via the sequence

$$R—X \xrightarrow{\text{M}} R—M—X \xrightarrow{X'_2} R—X' \qquad (7\text{--}33)^{53b}$$

More importantly, however, when the metal alkyl arises from other precursors (hydrocarbons, ethers or lower homologs), the action of molecular halogen or positive halogen agents furnishes an excellent route to halides. With more reactive RM and RX types, coupling to R—R may be a serious competitor (Eqs. 7–30 and 7–31).

Certain organic halides which also contain carbon-metal bonds deserve some discussion in this section. Special interest centers on types whose C—X and C—M bonds are α, β, or γ to each other. Being labile in many cases, the synthesis and decomposition of certain systems are noteworthy:

$$R_2Al—Cl \xrightarrow{CH_2N_2} RAl—CH_2—Cl \xrightarrow[-R_2AlCl]{>C=C<} \quad \overset{|}{\underset{|}{-C}}\!\!-\!\!\overset{|}{\underset{|}{C}}\!\!- \qquad (7\text{--}34)^{54}$$

$$R_3SiCH=CH_2 \xrightarrow{HX} R_3Si—CH_2CH_2—X \xrightarrow[-R_3SiX]{} CH_2=CH_2 \qquad (7\text{--}35)^{55}$$

$$R_2B—H \xrightarrow{CH_2=CHCH_2X} R_2B—CH_2—CH_2—CH_2—X \xrightarrow{-R_2BX} \triangle \qquad (7\text{--}36)^{56}$$

The smooth reaction of phenyl(trihalomethyl)mercury compounds with olefins[48b] fits this formal reaction pattern, but intermediate organomercury adducts have not as yet been detected. The first two equations yield a net outcome in accord with carbene addition and protodesilylation, respectively.

[53b] Cf. F. R. Jensen and L. H. Gale, *ibid.*, **82**, 148 (1960) and D. E. Applequist and A. H. Peterson, *ibid.*, **83**, 862 (1961), for the nonstereospecific cleavage of the carbon-metal bond seemingly to be involved in cleavages by halogen.

[54] H. Hoberg, *Ann.*, **656**, 1 (1962).

[55] (a) E. Larsson, *Trans. Chalmers Univ. Technol, Gothenburg*, **115**, 25 (1951); through *C.A.*, **47**, 10470 (1953); (b) L. H. Sommer, G. T. Kerr, and F. C. Whitmore, *J. Am. Chem. Soc.*, **70**, 434 (1948).

[56] M. F. Hawthorne and J. A. Dupont, *J. Am. Chem. Soc.*, **80**, 5831 (1958).

However, the detection of intermediates suggests a discrete elimination step.

Alcohols and Mercaptans

Of the two most general syntheses of these types, the addition of metal alkyls to carbonyl or thiocarbonyl derivatives and the cleavage of C—M bonds by oxygen or by sulfur, the first is so adequately treated elsewhere, as to require only a brief sketch. Development of the second is of much more recent vintage. The general accessibility of Group IIIA metal alkyls by metal hydride additions to olefins or acetylenes provides feasible starting materials for alcohol or mercaptan production. Indeed, the prominence of particular metal alkyls is neatly complementary in the two methods. Alkyls of sodium, lithium, and magnesium display a high reactivity toward carbonyl substrates, but the corresponding metal hydrides have little value in forming metal alkyls from unsaturated compounds. Group IIIA metal hydrides add to unsaturated hydrocarbons very smoothly, but the corresponding alkyls do not respond to carbonyl compounds in a feasible manner. Often only one carbon-metal bond of R_3M reacts, and Meerwein-Ponndorf-Verley side reactions can predominate:

$$R-Al(O-\overset{\overset{\displaystyle O}{\|}}{C}R)_2 \xleftarrow{\ R_3Al\ } O{=}C{=}O \xrightarrow{\ RMgX\ } R-C\overset{\nearrow O}{\searrow_{OMgX}} \qquad (7\ 37)[57]$$

$$(RCH_2CH_2)_3Al \xleftarrow{\ R_3Al\ } H_2C{=}CH_2 \xrightarrow{\ RMgX\ } N.R. \qquad (7\text{--}38)[58]$$

The interaction of every conceivable carbonyl and thiocarbonyl derivative with Grignard reagents has been explored. In evaluating the utility of corresponding sodium and lithium reagents, workers have found that the heightened reactivity of alkali metal alkyls is not always advantageous. The saline character of sodium alkyls make them insoluble in hydrocarbons and tends to cause metalative decomposition of almost any other solvent. Though of limited stability in ethers, lithium alkyls can be prepared and consumed in such media. These reagents are less sensitive to steric effects than Grignard reagents (Eq. 7–39). Side reactions, such as reduction via metal hydride [59, 60] (Eq. 7–40), enolization (Eq. 7–1), and 1,4-addition (Eq. 7–39), are thereby suppressed, as is apparent from the following cases:

[57] K. Ziegler, F. Krupp, K. Weyer, and W. Larbig, *Ann.*, **629**, 251 (1960).
[58] K. Ziegler, H.-G. Gellert, H. Lehmkuhl, W. Pfohl, and K. Zosel, *Ann.*, **629**, 1 (1960).
[59] M. S. Kharasch and S. Weinhouse, *J. Org. Chem.*, **1**, 209 (1936).
[60] C. C. Barker and G. Hallas, *J. Chem. Soc.*, **1961**, 1395.

$$\text{N.R.} \xleftarrow[25°]{\text{RMgBr}^{61}} (C_6H_5)_2C{=}NC_6H_5 \xrightarrow[25°]{\text{RLi}^{63}} \underset{\underset{C_6H_5}{|}}{\overset{\overset{C_6H_5}{|}}{R-C-NHC_6H_5}} \qquad (7\text{-}39)$$

$$100° \Big| \text{RMgBr}^{62}$$

$$\downarrow$$

$$\underset{\text{(aromatic ring with -R)}}{\overset{C_6H_5}{\diagdown}\overset{}{C-N}\overset{C_6H_5}{\diagup}\underset{H}{\diagdown}}$$

$$\underset{\underset{C_6H_5}{|}}{\overset{\overset{C_6H_5}{|}}{H-C-OH}} \xleftarrow[\text{(CH}_3)_2\text{CHCH}_2\text{MgBr}}^{59} \underset{C_6H_5}{\overset{C_6H_5}{\diagdown}}C{=}O \xrightarrow[\text{(CH}_3)_2\text{CHCH}_2\text{Li}]{60} (CH_3)_2CHCH_2-\underset{\underset{C_6H_5}{|}}{\overset{\overset{C_6H_5}{|}}{C}}-OH$$

$$(7\text{-}40)$$

The tendency of lithium alkyls to cause metalation of aromatic substrates and to add to functional groups inert to Grignard reagents can be troublesome and should not be forgotten:

$$R{-}M \xrightarrow{CO_2} R{-}\overset{\overset{O}{\diagup}}{C}\underset{O-M}{\diagdown} \xrightarrow{R{-}M} R{-}\underset{\underset{R}{|}}{\overset{\overset{O-M}{|}}{C}}{-}O{-}M \xrightarrow{H_2O} R_2C{=}O \qquad (7\text{-}41)$$

$$\begin{matrix} (M = MgX,) & & (M = Li,) \\ \text{(sole product)} & & \text{(by-product)} \end{matrix}$$

The second principal synthesis of alcohols depends upon the smoothness with which C—M bonds of feasible origin can be oxidized:

$$R{-}M \xrightarrow{O_2} R{-}O{-}O{-}M \xrightarrow{R{-}M} R{-}O{-}M \xrightarrow{H_2O} R{-}OH \qquad (7\text{-}42)$$

Unfortunately, radical-induced side reactions can intervene, lowering the yield by coupling to R—R or through solvent attack. Ethers appear to be especially prone to undesirable side reactions, and phenyl ethers or hydrocarbons may be used to advantage.[64] The metal alkyls stable to hydrolysis can be oxidized effectively with alkaline hydrogen peroxide.[65] Therefore, it

[61] W. F. Short and J. S. Watt, *J. Chem. Soc.*, **1930**, 2293.
[62] H. Gilman, J. E. Kirby, and C. R. Kinney, *J. Am. Chem. Soc.*, **51**, 2252 (1929).
[63] H. Gilman and R. H. Kirby, *J. Am. Chem. Soc.*, **57**, 1267 (1935).
[64] H. Gilman and A. Wood, *J. Am. Chem. Soc.*, **48**, 806 (1926).
[65] H. C. Brown and B. C. Subba Rao, *J. Am. Chem. Soc.*, **81**, 6423 (1959).

remains to decide on what a feasible RM type might be. Of greatest interest are those metal alkyls arising from the metalation of a hydrocarbon or from additions of MH or RM to olefins or acetylenes. The "anti-Markownikoff hydration" of olefins and acetylenes (Eqs. 7–43 and 7–44), the synthesis of fatty alcohols from ethylene (Eq. 7–45), and the conversion of aryl halides to phenols (Eq. 7–46) are valuable applications of this approach. The parallel behavior of organoidal-metallic systems (Eq. 7–47) also merits note.

$$3RCH{=}CH_2 \xrightarrow[M=Al,\,Ga,\,B]{MH_3} (RCH_2CH_2)_3M \xrightarrow[H_2O_2/NaOH(M=B)]{O_2\,(M=Al,\,Ga)} 3RCH_2CH_2OH$$

$$(7\text{–}43)^{66,67,68}$$

$$R{-}C{\equiv}C{-}H \xrightarrow{MH_3} \left[\underset{H}{\overset{R}{>}}C{=}C\underset{}{\overset{H}{<}} \right]_3 M \xrightarrow{(O)} H{-}\overset{\overset{O}{\|}}{C}{-}CH_2{-}R \qquad (7\text{–}44)^{69}$$

$$(CH_3CH_2)_3Al \xrightarrow{CH_2{=}CH_2} \left(\begin{array}{l} CH_3CH_2(CH_2CH_2)_x \\ CH_3CH_2(CH_2CH_2)_y{-} \\ CH_3CH_2(CH_2CH_2)_z \end{array} \right) Al \longrightarrow CH_3CH_2(CH_2CH_2)_aOH$$

$$a = 4\text{–}30,\ \text{even}$$
$$(7\text{–}45)^{66,\,70}$$

$$(7\text{–}46)^{71}$$

$$(C_6H_5)_3SiM \xrightarrow[2.\ RX]{1.\ S} (C_6H_5)_3Si{-}SR \qquad\qquad (7\text{–}47)^{72}$$

Carbonyl and Thiocarbonyl Derivatives

For the preparation of these types a highly reactive metal alkyl reagent stands at a distinct disadvantage, and the specific reagent and experimental conditions must be chosen for selectivity. Since the final product upon hydrolysis contains a reactive, unsaturated linkage, the reaction conditions must either be mild or the carbonyl group must be masked in the presence of any excess R′M. Thus in the following proposed scheme (Eq. 7–48), either

[66] K. Ziegler, F. Krupp, and K. Zosel, *Ann.*, **629**, 241 (1960).
[67] J. J. Eisch, *J. Am. Chem. Soc.*, **84**, 3830 (1962).
[68] H. C. Brown, *Hydroboration*, Benjamin, New York, 1962.
[69] H. C. Brown and G. Zweifel, *J. Am. Chem. Soc.*, **81**, 1512 (1959).
[70] K. Ziegler, H.-G. Gellert, K. Zosel, E. Holzkamp, J. Schneider, M. Söll, and W.-R. Kroll, *Ann.*, **629**, 121 (1960).
[71] M. F. Hawthorne, *J. Org. Chem.*, **22**, 1001 (1957).
[72] H. Gilman and G. D. Lichtenwalter, *J. Org. Chem.*, **25**, 1064 (1960).

$$R-C\overset{O}{\underset{Z}{\diagdown}} \xrightarrow[\substack{\text{step 1}\\ k_1}]{R'M} R-\overset{O-M}{\underset{\underset{Z}{|}}{\overset{|}{C}}}-R' \xrightarrow[\substack{\text{step 2}\\ k_2}]{-MZ} R-\overset{O}{\overset{||}{C}}-R' \xrightarrow[\substack{\text{step 3}\\ k_3}]{R'M} R-\overset{OM}{\underset{\underset{R'}{|}}{\overset{|}{C}}}-R' \qquad (7\text{-}48)$$

IV

k_1 must be $\gg k_2$ or $k_1 \gg k_3$. With Grignard reagents, usually $k_1 \lesssim k_2$; therefore, esters and acid anhydrides lead easily to tertiary alcohols. Only by operating at low temperatures and with inverse addition (introduction of R'M to RCOZ) can acceptable yields of ketones be obtained. With carboxylic acid salts (Z = OM), k_1 is often $\ll k_3$, especially with M = MgX. Because of the rate difference, the carbonation of R'M with CO_2 to yield RCO_2M proceeds in high yield. As the reactivity of R'M (M = Li, Na) or the covalent character of RCO_2M(M = Li, Al) increases, however, even salts of carboxylic acids tend to give increasing proportions of ketones (via IV, Z = OM) and tertiary alcohols ($k_2 \simeq k_1$, via RR'C=O). Purposive aldehyde or ketone syntheses have resulted from making Z in intermediate IV a poor leaving group (Z = $R_2\ddot{N}$, OLi)[73]:

$$(7\text{-}49)$$

Alternatively, the selective ease with which acyl halides, but not esters or ketones, respond to zinc, cadmium, and sometimes mercury alkyls can be a fruitful route to ketones[22, 73b] (Eq. 7–50). It might also be recalled in this

$$\overset{O}{\overset{||}{R-C-Cl}} \xrightarrow{R'MZ} \overset{O}{\overset{||}{R-C-R'}} + MZCl \qquad (7\text{-}50)$$

connection that α,β-unsaturated carbonyl compounds exhibit a pronounced tendency to yield β-substituted saturated carbonyl derivatives with less reactive metal alkyls. The competition between such 1,4-addition and normal 1,2-addition is typified in the behavior of benzalacetophenone (Table 7–1). Finally, the low reactivity toward Grignard reagents which nitriles exhibit in the Johnson-Entemann competition scale[74] can be utilized for ketone syn-

[73] (a) G. Wittig, *Angew. Chem.*, **53**, 241 (1940); (b) cf. J. Kollonitsch, *J. Chem. Soc.*, **1966**, 453, 456, for the ambiguities concerning the inherent reactivity of cadmium alkyls. Apparently magnesium salts catalyze the interaction of cadmium alkyls with acid halides.

[74] M. S. Kharasch and O. Reinmuth, *Grignard Reactions of Nonmetallic Substances*, Prentice-Hall, Englewood Cliffs, N.J., 1954, pp. 767–845.

TABLE 7–1

The Addition of Organometallics to Benzalacetophenone[a]

$$C_6H_5-\overset{\overset{\displaystyle H}{|}}{C}=\overset{\displaystyle O}{\overset{||}{C}}-\overset{}{C}-C_6H_5 \xrightarrow[\text{2. } H_2O]{\text{1. RM}} C_6H_5-\overset{\overset{\displaystyle H}{|}}{C}=\overset{\overset{\displaystyle OH}{|}}{C}-C(C_6H_5)_2 + (C_6H_5)_2CHCH_2-\overset{\displaystyle O}{\overset{||}{C}}-C_6H_5$$

RM	% 1,2	% 1,4
C_6H_5K	52	0
C_6H_5CaI	45	0
C_6H_5Na	39	3.5
C_6H_5Li	69	13
C_6H_5MgBr	0	94
C_6H_5MnI	0	77
$(C_6H_5)Be$	0	90
$(C_6H_5)_2Zn$	0	91
$(C_6H_5)_2Cd$	0	100
$(C_6H_5)_3Al$	0	94

[a] H. Gilman and R. H. Kirby, *J. Am. Chem. Soc.*, **63**, 2046 (1941).

thesis. The imino salts usually are stable toward excess RM; thus their hydrolysis provides high yields of ketone. However, exceptionally reactive metal alkyls ($CH_2=CHCH_2MgBr$, C_2H_5Li) can lead to trisubstituted methylamines:

$$R-C\equiv N \xrightarrow{R'M} \underset{V}{\overset{R}{\underset{R'}{>}}C=N\diagdown_M} \xrightarrow{H_3O^+} \overset{R}{\underset{R'}{>}}C=O \qquad (7\text{-}51)^{74}$$

$$\downarrow R'M$$

$$\overset{R'}{\underset{R''}{\overset{|}{R-C-N}}}\diagup^M_M \xrightarrow{H_2O} \overset{R'}{\underset{R''}{\overset{|}{R-C-NH_2}}} \qquad (7\text{-}52)^{75}$$

The hydroformylation of olefins in the oxo process leads to aldehydes via intermediates V and VI[76a] (Eq. 7–53). The behavior of transition metal

[75] B. B. Allen and H. R. Henze, *J. Am. Chem. Soc.*, **61**, 1790 (1939).
[76] (a) R. F. Heck and D. S. Breslow, *J. Am. Chem. Soc.*, **83**, 4023 (1961); (b) cf. R. F. Heck, *ibid.*, **85**, 2013 (1963), for similar views of the carboxylation of allylic halides by nickel carbonyl.

hydrides in adding to alkenes and of the resulting alkyls in undergoing carbonylation parallels that of main group compounds.[76b]

$$H\text{—}Co(CO)_3 \xrightarrow{RCH=CH_2} RCH_2CH_2\text{—}Co(CO)_3 \xrightarrow{CO} RCH_2CH_2\text{—}Co(CO)_4$$

VIa   VI   (7–53)

$$H\text{—}Co(CO)_3 + RCH_2CH_2\overset{H}{\underset{}{\text{—}C}}\text{=}O \xleftarrow{H_2} RCH_2CH_2\overset{O}{\overset{\|}{\text{—}C}}\text{—}Co(CO)_3 \longleftarrow$$

Amines, Nitriles, and Azomethines

In general, certain of these structural types are available via metal alkyls, if appropriate nitrogen derivatives are employed. To obtain amines, some amino derivative containing an $R_2N\text{—}Z$ ($Z = O, X$) linkage is suitable. If $R = H$, then an excess of the metal alkyl might be needed, in order to consume the active hydrogens[77]:

$$\underset{R}{\overset{Li}{\diagdown\diagup}} \xrightarrow[\text{2. H}_3\text{O}^+]{\text{1. CH}_3\text{O—NLi}_2} \underset{R}{\overset{NH_2}{\diagdown\diagup}} \qquad (7\text{–}54)$$

For aromatic derivatives this method has uncommon value where the organometallic may be accessible from the corresponding halogen or hydrocarbon derivative by halogen-metal or hydrogen-metal exchange. In aliphatic and alicyclic systems the organoboranes resulting from the hydroboration of unsaturated hydrocarbons can be converted into amino derivatives particularly smoothly (Eq. 7–55). The resistance of carbon-boron bonds to protolysis by the acidic hydrogens of chloramine or hydroxylamine-O-sulfonic acid permits high yields of amines to be obtained. With magnesium alkyls and chloramine there is evidence of N—Cl bond cleavage in the reverse sense (Eq. 7–56).

$$3R\text{—}CH=CH_2 \xrightarrow[\text{THF}]{BH_3} (RCH_2CH_2)_3B \xrightarrow{ClNH_2} RCH_2CH_2\text{—}NH_2 \qquad (7\text{–}55)^{78}$$

$$C_2H_5MgCl \xrightarrow{ClNH_2} \underset{39\%}{C_2H_5\text{—}Cl} + \underset{57\%}{C_2H_5\text{—}NH_2} \qquad (7\text{–}56)^{79}$$

[77] N. I. Sheverdina and K. A. Kocheshkov, *J. Gen. Chem. USSR*, (*English Transl.*), **8**, 1825 (1938); through *C.A.*, **33**, 5804 (1933).
[78] H. C. Brown, W. R. Heydkamp, E. Breuer, and W. S. Murphy, *J. Am. Chem. Soc.*, **86**, 3565 (1964).
[79] G. H. Coleman, J. L. Hermanson and H. L. Johnson, *J. Am. Chem. Soc.*, **59**, 1896 (1937).

The synthesis of azomethine (Schiff base) systems by means of metal alkyls appears to be generally applicable. Several approaches are available: (a) the careful protolysis of the salts formed from nitriles and metal alkyls (V in Eq. 7–51) permits the isolation of imines; (b) treatment of N-substituted amides with PCl_5 yields imino chlorides, $RClC=NR$, which can interact smoothly with RM to yield fully substituted Schiff bases[80]:

$$(7\text{–}57)$$

and (c) partially substituted azomethines can add RM (RLi or RMgX) and the adduct caused to re-form the fully substituted Schiff base by hydride loss or by oxidation:

$$(7\text{–}58)$$

These foregoing alkylations are extremely useful in obtaining substituted aza-aromatic hydrocarbons.[81, 82]

With highly reactive RM types, it is obvious that the final nitrogen products of the foregoing processes will tend to be saturated (amines). Hence, certain highly branched primary and secondary amines may be uniquely accessible by this route[82c, 83]:

$$(7\text{–}59)$$

[80] H. Gilman and J. A. Beel, *J. Am. Chem. Soc.*, **73**, 774 (1951).
[81] (a) K. Ziegler and H. Zeiser, *Ann.*, **485**, 174 (1931); (b) O. Cervinka, *Chem. Ind.*(*London*), 1482 (1960).
[82] (a) E. Bergmann and W. Rosenthal, *J. prakt. Chem.*, **135**, 267 (1932); (b) H. Gilman and S. Spatz, *J. Am. Chem. Soc.*, **63**, 1553 (1941); (c) H. Gilman and J. Eisch, *ibid.*, **79**, 2150, 4423 (1957).
[83] (a) H. Gilman and G. C. Gainer, *J. Am. Chem. Soc.*, **69**, 877 (1947); (b) H. Gilman and R. D. Nelson, *ibid.*, **70**, 3316 (1948).

Metalloid and Nonmetalloid Derivatives

The establishment of carbon bonds to all but the most electronegative elements can be accomplished by choice of the appropriate metal alkyl. In discussing the synthesis of less reactive metal alkyls, from more reactive types, the reasons favoring the exchange of alkyl groups between metal centers were analyzed (Chapter Six). Similar energetic considerations permit the synthesis of alkyls of metalloids or nonmetallic elements:

$$nRM + EZ_n \longrightarrow ER_n + nMZ \tag{7-60}$$

For a polyvalent element E, the ligands Z may be replaced in a step-wise fashion, depending upon the reactivity of RM and upon the experimental conditions. Whether the mixed alkyls, $R_m EZ_{n-m}$, are isolable in turn is dependent on their thermodynamic or kinetic stability to symmetrization ($R_m EZ_{n-m} \rightarrow ER_m + EZ_m$). It should be apparent that successful, step-wise alkylation leading to mixed alkyls, $R_1 R_2 R_3 R_m E$, opens up vistas of studying the stereochemistry and the structure of such organoelement compounds. The recent research with optically active organosilanes[84] and germanes,[85] as well as *cis*- and *trans*-geometrical isomers of platinum,[86] illustrate the future implications to chemistry of this synthetic entree:

$$[(C_2H_5)_3P]_2 PtCl_2 + 2C_6H_5Li \longrightarrow \begin{matrix} (C_2H_5)_3P \\ (C_2H_5)_3P \end{matrix} Pt \begin{matrix} C_6H_5 \\ C_6H_5 \end{matrix} + 2LiCl \tag{7-62}$$

A second aspect of synthesizing element alkyls is that this often permits the study of the formal, higher valence states of these elements. In the addition to the easily isolable, well-characterized R_3Au, R_3Tl, and R_4Pb, the alkylation of suitable element halides, EX_n, has permitted the isolation of $(C_6H_5)_3I$, $(C_6H_5)_4Te$,[87] and $(C_6H_5)_5Sb$,[88] as well as the previously elusive

[84] L. H. Sommer, K. W. Michael, and W. D. Korte, *J. Am. Chem. Soc.*, **85**, 3712 (1963).
[85] A. G. Brook and G. J. D. Peddle, *J. Am. Chem. Soc.*, **85**, 1869 (1963).
[86] J. Chatt and B. L. Shaw, *J. Chem. Soc.*, **1959**, 4020.
[87] G. Wittig and H. Fritz, *Ann.*, **577**, 39 (1952).
[88] G. Wittig and K. Clauss, *Ann.*, **577**, 26 (1952).

derivatives of higher valent transition metals, $(C_6H_5)_3Cr$,[89] $(CH_3)_4Ti$,[90] and $(CH_2{=}CHCH_2)_nM$.[91] With transition metals, auxiliary complexation with Lewis bases and supplemental π-bonding seem essential in isolating the derivative (see Chapter Six).

The experimental execution of the particular alkylation involves many specialized considerations that cannot be entertained at this time. However, certain general observations are in order. First, to favor partial alkylation, the alkylating agent RM should be added to the element derivative, EZ_n (where $Z = X$, OR, or H) slowly at as low a temperature as is feasible (inverse addition). Second, to achieve complete alkylation of EZ_n or $R_m{'}EZ_{n-m}$, it is often necessary to use the most reactive RM (lithium or sodium alkyls) in generous excess at elevated temperatures. Especially where the fully alkylated product, ER_n, contains serious steric congestion around the element center, will the complete alkylation of EZ_n present problems. For example, the attempted syntheses of tetra-α-naphthylsilane have given only negative results.[92] Treatment of $Si(OC_2H_5)_4$ with α-naphthyllithium at 170–180°C yields only ethoxytri-α-naphthylsilane.

Third, the use of strongly donor solvents or of the substrate in donor complexes, EZ_nY_m ($Y = OR_2$, NR_3, PR_3, AsR_3) often speeds the alkylation process and/or stabilizes the resulting element alkyl. As mentioned previously, the stabilization thereby enjoyed has permitted the establishment of σ-carbon-metal bonds with transition metals. Fourth, despite the best choice of experimental conditions, partial alkylation may be difficult to achieve, because of similar rates for successive steps ($k_1 \simeq k_2 \simeq k_3$, etc.):

$$EZ_n \xrightarrow[k_1]{RM} REZ_{n-1} \xrightarrow[k_2]{RM} R_2EZ_{n-2} \xrightarrow[k_3]{RM} R_3EZ_{n-3} \qquad (7\text{--}63)$$

In this situation, it may prove beneficial to isolate the fully alkylated product, R_nZ, and to exchange some of the groups in a separate step. This might be done by a cleavage reaction or by redistribution. These products, in turn, could be alkylated by a different agent, R'M. The following synthesis of a mixed alkyl typifies this approach[93]:

$$SnCl_4 \xrightarrow{C_6H_5MgBr} (C_6H_5)_4Sn \xrightarrow{SnCl_4} (C_6H_5)_3SnCl \xrightarrow{CH_2{=}CHCH_2MgX} (C_6H_5)_3Sn{-}C_3H_5$$

$$(7\text{--}64)$$

[89] W. Herwig and H. H. Zeiss, *J. Am. Chem. Soc.*, **79**, 6561 (1957).

[90] K. Clauss and C. Beermann, *Angew. Chem.*, **71**, 627 (1959).

[91] G. Wilke and B. Bogdanovic, *Angew. Chem.*, **73**, 756 (1961).

[92] A. D. Petrov and V. S. Chuganov, *Dokl. Akad. Nauk SSSR*, **77**, 815 (1951); through *C.A.*, **46**, 480 (1952).

[93] H. Gilman and J. Eisch, *J. Org. Chem.*, **20**, 763 (1955).

Polymers

In the present context two types of polymers come to mind: polymers involving suitable unsaturated organometallics themselves as monomer components, and purely organic polymers prepared by the catalytic agency of metal alkyls. The former class, organometallic polymers, is certainly a topic of growing interest in industry,[94] but the field offers such complexity and diversity of behavior, that brief comments will have to suffice. The latter type of polymers has flourished for some fifty years, and the principles of organic polymerization are firmly established.[95] Nevertheless, in little more than the past decade, the introduction of organometallic polymerization catalysts has revolutionized the industrial practice and the mechanistic views of organic polymerization. The number of patents, scientific papers, and industrial researchers connected with these catalysts is overwhelming. Under these intimidating circumstances prudence allows only a few brief remarks in this survey.

The formation of organometallic polymers could arise from the behavior of a typically polymerizable organic group, as in the vinyl polymerization of vinylmetalloids of silicon or phosphorus. Or the metal centers could be exclusively involved in establishing new covalent bonds. Here the alkyl groups simply serve as pendants to the growing polymer chain. The polymer chain backbone could consist exclusively of metalloid atoms (all Si, Sn, Ge atoms) or of alternating metal and nonmetal (O, N, S) atoms. Illustrative of these are the cyclic oligomers of arsenic and tin $(C_6H_5AsAsC_6H_5)_3$[96] and $[(C_6H_5)_2Sn]$,[97] where concatenation of metalloid atoms occurs, on the one hand, and the silicones, where a regular interlinking of silicon and oxygen atoms forms a chain for appended alkyl or aryl groups, on the other hand:

$$\left(\!\!\begin{array}{c} R \\ | \\ O\!-\!Si \\ | \\ R \end{array}\!\!\right)_{\!\!x}$$

The third type of organometallic polymer demands the cooperation of both the metal and the organic group of the metal alkyl. The most common type would be an organometallic monomer whose R contains carbon-carbon unsaturation and whose metal center has a reactive C—M or H—M linkage.

[94] D. Braun, *Angew. Chem.*, **73**, 197 (1961).
[95] C. S. Marvel, *An Introduction to the Organic Chemistry of High Polymers*, Wiley, New York, 1959.
[96] S. R. Rasmussen and J. Danielson, *Acta Chem. Scand.*, **14**, 1862 (1960).
[97] W. P. Neumann and K. König, *Angew. Chem.*, **74**, 215 (1962).

Thus, the thermal or radical-catalyzed polymerization of ω-alkenyl-aluminum[98] or ω-alkenyltin hydrides[99] would be cases in point:

$$x CH_2\!\!=\!\!CH(CH_2)_n Sn(CH_3)_2 H \longrightarrow [-CH_2-CH_2(CH_2)_n \overset{\displaystyle CH_3}{\underset{\displaystyle CH_3}{\mid}} Sn-]_x \qquad (7\text{--}65)$$

A more restricted type of polymerization whose aggregation often can be sundered by solvation alone is electron-deficient bonding in certain metal alkyls. Dimethylberyllium and diphenylmagnesium are composed of a linear series of metal atoms held together by tetrahedrally disposed bridges of the organic groups. The macromolecular structure then is simply a polymeric extension of the bonding encountered in the dimer of trimethylaluminum.

Although it was fashionable in the 1950s to speak of polymerization by organometallic catalysts as anionic polymerization, this term is inadequate to describe all of the ramified experimental findings. Just as a carbanionic view of organometallic reaction mechanisms is of limited validity (see Chapter Five), so a similar interpretation of polymerization is not always applicable. A deeper probing of the feasible catalyst combinations, kinetics, stereo-chemistry of polymerizations, and the physical properties of the polymers has made a plurality of mechanisms essential to a rational understanding. Although anionic polymerization still seems to describe the behavior of alkali metal alkyls toward conjugated dienes, the intervention of other mechanisms is indicated for such agents as boron alkyls in the presence of oxygen (free radical), aluminum, or gallium alkyls in combination with transition metal halides or alkoxides (Ziegler-Natta catalysts involving organometallic π-complexes), and alkylaluminum halides (electrophilic catalysts). The striking feature of the Ziegler-Natta catalysts is the precise stereoregularity with which olefins and dienes can be polymerized. In the first place, the type of stereochemistry exhibited by the monomer unit can involve the configuration of the asymmetric tertiary carbon atom in 1,2-polymerization of olefins. The configuration of this tertiary carbon in head-to-tail polymers can be the same (VIII, isotactic sequence), can alternate for successive carbons of the chain (IX, syndiotactic sequence), or can be ran-domly different (X, atactic sequence). In the second place, with conjugate dienes, the monomer units can have geometrically different *cis*-1,4- (XI) or *trans*-1,4 (XII) linkages. Whether a given polymer is made up of identically bonded monomer units, or of mixtures of configuration, has a profound influence on macroscopic properties, such as melting point, tensile strength,

[98] B. Bartocha, A. J. Bilbo, D. E. Bublitz, and M. Y. Gran, *Z. Naturforsch.*, **166**, 953 (1962).
[99] J. G. Noltes and G. J. M. van der Kerk, *Chimia*, **16**, 122 (1962).
[100] G. Natta, *Angew. Chem.*, **76**, 553 (1964).

TABLE 7–2

Physical Properties of Stereoregular Polymers of Butadiene

Polymer (% Purity)	m.p.	Recurrency Period (Å)	Density (g/ml)
trans-1,4 (XII, 99–100%)	146	4.85 (modif. 1)	0.97
		4.65 (modif. 2)	0.93
cis-1,4 (XI, 98–99%)	2	8.6	1.01
isotactic-1,2 (VIII, 99%)	126	6.5	0.96
syndiotactic-1,2 (IX, 99%)	156	5.14	0.96

[a] G. Natta, *Angew. Chem.*, **76**, 553 (1964).

and density. By employing various combinations of Ziegler-Natta catalysts, for example, butadiene has been polymerized in separate experiments to yield the four stereoregular polymers, VIII, IX, XI, and XII, each in better than 98% configurational purity. The divergence in the physical properties of the polymers is evident from inspection of Table 7–2.[100] Hence, the extensive industrial research on the mechanisms of these stereoregular polymerizations.

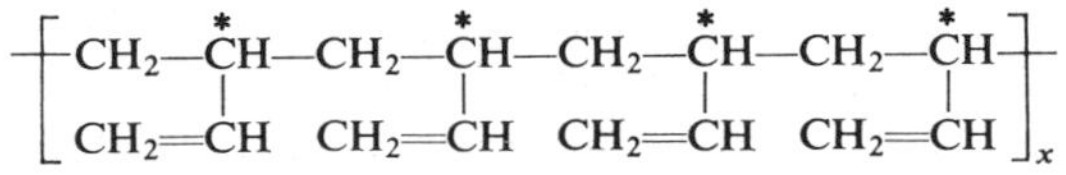

$$\left[\text{CH}_2-\overset{*}{\text{C}}\text{H}-\text{CH}_2-\overset{*}{\text{C}}\text{H}-\text{CH}_2-\overset{*}{\text{C}}\text{H}-\text{CH}_2-\overset{*}{\text{C}}\text{H}\right]_x$$

(with CH$_2$=CH substituents)

VIII

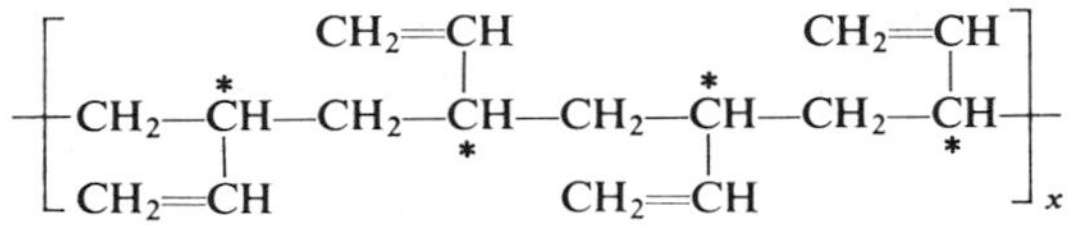

IX

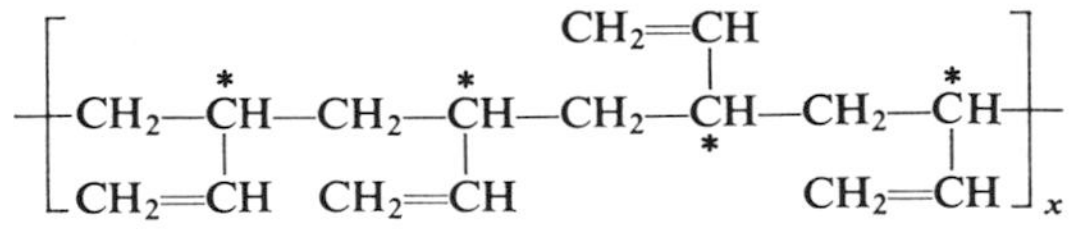

X

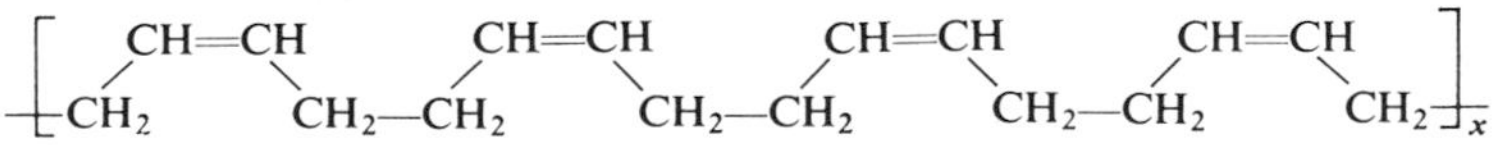

XI

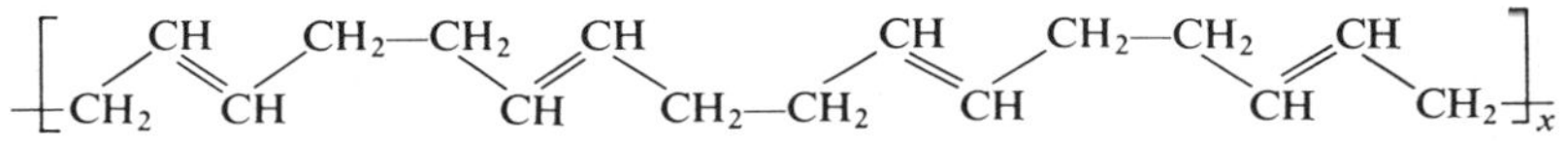

XII

EIGHT

Special Topics in Organometallic Chemistry

In this section attention will be directed to certain aspects of specific organometallic compounds, where the interest lies in structural and reaction properties not directly associated with the principal carbon-metal bond. As will be seen, this may lead to a consideration of supplemental carbon-metal bonding or to the bonding properties within the attached organic group. The number of such special topics undoubtedly will grow, and inherent in each topic considered below is the ability to become a fascinating and independent area of research.

Ferrocenes

As the prototype of transition metal arene complexes possessing synthetic accessibility, chemical versatility, and yet remarkable structural stability, ferrocene has received the particular attention of the organic chemist. From another vantage point, it embodies the arresting bonding properties of transition metal π-complexes, and hence it has been scrutinized exhaustively by physical inorganic chemists. The theoretical superstructure of organometallic π-complexes, being both ramified and formidable, cannot be given in this book, but the interested reader should refer to several recent treatments

143

for the various views of the chemical bonding.[1] Rather the purpose here is to present a sufficient background of theoretical conclusions to place the extraordinary chemical and physical properties of ferrocene into a rational framework.

From a number of different vantage points, ferrocene is a remarkable substance: as an organometallic compound, the bonding between the cyclopentadienyl group and the iron atom is resistant to hydrolytic and oxidative cleavage; as a cyclopentadienyl derivative, it does not show any facile diene behavior; as a possible ferrous or neutral iron derivative, it is oxidizable reversibly to the ferricinium ion, and as an unsaturated organic derivative, it undergoes substitution, rather than addition, reactions. These observations have caused organic chemists to term ferrocene an aromatic system: that is, a ring system of $4n + 2\pi$-electrons that has exceptional stability and in reactions tends to preserve ultimately its structure. Possibly prompted by its synthesis from the cyclopentadienides ($C_5H_5^-M^+$), themselves aromatic systems, one might view ferrocene as $(C_5H_5^-)_2Fe^{++}$. This view is not in agreement with its properties. Nor would a σ-bonded cyclopentadienyl-iron linkage be a reasonable representation. Structural data, moreover, demonstrate the equivalence of all carbon-iron separations and the sandwich array of the two cyclopentadienyl rings about the metal atom. The rotational barrier of the two rings about the C_5H_5—Fe—C_5H_5 axis is low, but at ordinary temperatures the ring hydrogens are staggered[2] (I).

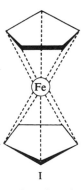

I

The molecular orbital accounting for these structural data involves not only bonding of π-electrons from the cyclopentadienyl group to the hybrid-

[1] (a) M. Rosenblum, *Chemistry of the Iron Group Metallocenes: Ferrocene, Ruthenocene and Osmocene*, Wiley (Interscience), New York, 1965; (b) G. Wilkinson and F. A. Cotton in *Progress in Inorganic Chemistry*, Vol. 1 (F. A. Cotton, ed.), Wiley (Interscience), New York, 1959, Chap. 1; (c) E. O. Fischer and H. P. Fritz, in *Advances in Inorganic Chemistry and Radiochemistry*, Vol. 1 (H. J. Emeleus and A. G. Sharpe, eds.), Academic, New York, 1959, pp. 56–117.
[2] J. D. Dunitz, L. E. Orgel, and A. Rich, *Acta Cryst.*, **9**, 373 (1956).

ized *d*-orbitals of the iron, but the back-donation of electrons from the filled *d*-orbitals of iron to the unoccupied antibonding π-orbitals of the hydrocarbon rings. Noteworthy is the delocalization of the π-electrons throughout both rings, explaining why the ion-pair picture, $(C_5H_5^-)_2Fe^{++}$, and the σ-bonded system, $(\sigma\text{-}C_5H_5)_2Fe$, are not acceptable. Although the π-electrons of the organic group are by no means the exclusive property of either metal or organic group, they can be thought of as furnishing an electronic cloud similar to an element of higher atomic number. A simple rule thereby emerges for predicting the number of π- and σ-donor ligands which will form stable complexes with transition metal centers. As an extension of the general rule that atoms tend to implicate all their available, low-lying orbitals in chemical bonding (corollaries: rule of two and rule of eight), Sidgwick's effective atomic number (e.a.n.) rule states that elements react chemically, in order to achieve the closed shell configuration of the rare gases.[3] Hence, iron in ferrocene would have an e.a.n. of 36 ($Fe^{++} = 24 + 2C_5H_5^- - 12$ for c.a.n. of 36, that is, krypton), but back-donation from iron tends to prevent an unacceptable concentration of negative charge on the metal. Subject to the inevitable exceptions, the e.a.n. rule nevertheless proves most illuminating in discerning stable arene complexes. Although transition metal complexes not obeying this rule are known, many are highly reactive and thus e.a.n. considerations are again valuable. Thus, although ferrocene does not respond to dienophiles, nickelocene (e.a.n. = 38) does[4]:

$$(C_5H_5)_2Ni \xrightarrow{\quad R-C\equiv C-R \quad} \text{II} \tag{8 1}$$

Note that the adduct II now satisfies the e.a.n. of 36.

The preparations of ferrocenes involve methods for complexing appropriate cyclopentadiene derivatives with Fe^0, Fe^{++}, or Fe^{+3} reagents or, alternatively, introducing substituents into the parent ferrocene system by organic transformations. The former class relies chiefly upon the nucleophilic attack of the cyclopentadienyl anion, $C_5H_5^-$, on Fe^{++} or Fe^{+3} salts (Eq. 8–2). The $C_5H_5^-$ is readily obtained from the acidic C_5H_6 and RNa, RLi, RMgBr, or

[3] (a) N. V. Sidgwick, *The Electronic Theory of Valency*, Clarendon, Oxford, 1927, Chap. 10; (b) A. A. Blanchard, *Chem. Rev.*, **26**, 409 (1940).
[4] M. Dubeck, *J. Am. Chem. Soc.*, **82**, 6193 (1960).
[5] G. Wilkinson, in *Organic Syntheses*, Coll. Vol. IV (N. Rabjohn, ed.), Wiley, New York, 1963, p. 473.

R_2NH.[5] Substituted cyclopentadienyl anions, obtained in a clever manner by the reductive dimerization of fulvenes, can also be employed[6]:

$$FeCl_2 \;+\; 2C_5H_5Na \;\longrightarrow\; (C_5H_5)_2Fe \;+\; 2NaCl \qquad (8\text{--}2)$$

$$\text{(fulvene)} \xrightarrow{\;2Na\;} \text{(cyclopentadienyl)}\!-\!CR_2\!-\!CR_2\!-\!\text{(cyclopentadienyl)}\;2Na^+ \xrightarrow{\;FeCl_2\;} \text{(bridged ferrocene)} \qquad (8\text{--}3)$$

Zerovalent iron, either as free metal or as a carbonyl, $Fe(CO)_5$, will attack cyclopentadiene directly to yield ferrocene or $(C_5H_5)_2Fe_2(CO)_4$, respectively. Parenthetically it might be added that these methods can be applied successfully to many other transition metal complexes.[7]

The introduction of substituents into the ferrocene nucleus itself is limited to nonoxidizing reagents. Since this excludes side chain oxidation, as well as direct halogenation or nitration, imaginative indirect methods must be pressed into service to obtain halo, nitro, and certain oxyalkyl ferrocenes. As compensation for this disadvantage, however, ferrocene can be readily metalated and the resulting organomercury and organo-alkali derivatives of ferrocene thereupon transformed into useful derivatives. In general, electrophilic substitution (R^+ and Lewis acidic RM) appears to proceed more readily with ferrocene than with benzene. The following syntheses (Eqs. 8–4 and 8–5, and Chart 8–1) exemplify the value of the substitution route to ferrocene derivatives[8,9]:

$$(C_5H_5)_2Fe \xrightarrow[\;AlCl_3\;]{3i\text{-}C_4H_8} [(t\text{-}C_4H_9)_2C_5H_3FeC_5H_4(t\text{-}C_4H_9)] \quad \text{alkyl} \qquad (8\text{--}4)$$
$$43.5\%$$

$$(C_5H_5)_2Fe \xrightarrow[\;2.\ H_3O^+\;]{1.\ C_6H_5\overset{\textstyle CH_3}{\underset{|}{N}}CHO/POCl_3} (C_5H_5)Fe(C_5H_4\!-\!\overset{\textstyle H}{C}\!=\!O) \quad \text{acyl} \qquad (8\text{--}5)$$
$$78\%$$

[6] K. L. Rinehart, Jr., et al., *J. Am. Chem. Soc.*, **82**, 4111 (1960).
[7] G. Wilkinson, F. A. Cotton, and J. M. Birmingham, *J. Inorg. Nucl. Chem.*, **2**, 95 (1956).
[8] K. Plesske, *Angew. Chem.*, **74**, 301 (1962).
[9] K. Plesske, *Angew. Chem.*, **74**, 347 (1962).

CHART 8–1

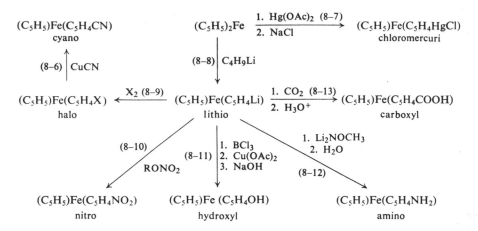

The structural characteristics of the ferrocene nucleus can now be discussed upon the basis of chemical and physical measurements for ferrocene itself and the behavior of substituents on the rings. The antiprismatic sandwich structure has been demonstrated beyond doubt by X-ray crystallographic analysis, the C—C bonds in a given ring (1.403 ± 0.02 Å) and all C—Fe bonds (2.045 ± 0.01 Å) being equidistant. This structure brings the following data into consonance; the essentially zero dipole moment; only one type of C—H bond in the infrared and n.m.r. spectra; the rather high diamagnetic susceptibility (suggestive of ring currents); and the failure to isolate conformational isomers (low C_5H_5—FeC_5H_5 rotational barrier). The electronic fine structure is revealed by the equilibrium and kinetic properties of ferrocenes. The finding is often stressed that in ferrocene derivatives the rings bear more negative character than the analogous benzene derivatives. Such a view should not be overdone, however, for ferrocene is patently not benzene, and indeed its character intuitively should be more related to the cyclopentadienyl anion, which clearly has, per carbon, 1.2 times the electron density of benzene. This negative character in the rings causes aminoferrocene to be more basic than aniline and ferrocenecarboxylic acid to be less acidic than benzoic acid.[10] Similar electron accessibility can also explain why ferrocene carboxaldehyde is more soluble in acidic solutions than in benzaldehyde (stability of conjugate

acid: $\underset{Fe\ +}{R—\overset{H}{\underset{|}{C}}—OH}$). This stabilization of carbonium ions *alpha* to a cyclopentadienyl ring seems operative in ferrocene reactions, where the positive character of the atom adjacent to the ring is important in determining the

[10] W. F. Little and R. Eisenthal, *J. Org. Chem.*, **26**, 3609 (1961).

activation energy of a reaction. The greater rate at which ferrocenylmethyl acetates undergo solvolysis, compared with benzyl counterparts, suggests that electron release lowers the energy of activation for the ionization step.[11] In the reverse sense, the saponification of ferrocenyl acetates is slower than that of phenyl acetates, apparently because the ground state of the ester is more

$$R \rightarrow O-\overset{\overset{\displaystyle O}{\|}}{C}-CH_3$$
$$Fe$$

III

stabilized in the former case (III). This greater stability effectively increases the activation energy necessary to attain the transition state (IV).

$$R-O-\overset{\overset{\displaystyle O^-}{|}}{\underset{\underset{\displaystyle OH}{|}}{C}}-CH_3$$
$$Fe$$

IV

The electron-rich nature of the hydrocarbon rings in ferrocene also is evident in the effect of oxidizing agents and other highly electrophilic reagents (halogen, nitrating agents); the metallocene system is thereby converted into ferricenium salts. Whether attack is at the outer faces of the rings or at the metal atom directly has not been demonstrated.[10, 12] It does appear in other cases, however, that electronic interplay between metal atom and the ring can be important. Thus, reactions suggestive of $C_5H_5Fe(II)C_5H_4—CH_2^+$ intermediates may permit the formation of its electronic isomer, $C_5H_5Fe(III)-C_5H_4—\dot{C}H_2$, and hence permit the coupling to *bis*-ferrocenylethane, $[C_6H_5Fe(II)C_5H_4—CH_2]_2$.[13] Further, there are spectroscopic data suggestive of a small rotational barrier for the rings but of very considerable electronic interaction between heteroannular substituents in ferrocene derivatives.[14]

The remarkable chemistry of ferrocene has occasioned a complete exploration of almost every conceivable metal cyclopentadienide. Indeed, representatives for each of the various alternative bonding types considered for ferrocene (ionic, σ-covalent unassociated, and σ-covalent associated) have been uncovered.[15] Thus in the first long period the derivatives of potassium, calcium,

[11] E. A. Hill and J. H. Richards, *J. Am. Chem. Soc.*, **83**, 4216 (1961).
[12] G. Winkhaus, L. Pratt, and G. Wilkinson, *J. Chem. Soc.*, **1961**, 3807, have found that the reduction of arenemanganese tricarbonyl cation by $NaBD_4$ yields the endo deuterio cyclohexadienylmanganese tricarbonyl. Presumably endo hydride attack is favored by preliminary Mn—H formation and subsequent rearrangement.
[13] K. L. Rinehart, Jr., C. J. Michejda, and P. A. Kittle, *J. Am. Chem. Soc.*, **81**, 3162 (1959).
[14] M. Rosenblum, *J. Am. Chem. Soc.*, **81**, 4530 (1959).
[15] M. D. Rausch, *J. Chem. Educ.*, **37**, 568 (1960).

scandium, titanium(II), and manganese(II) seem ionic and therefore are metal cyclopenta*dienides*, whereas those of germanium and following elements seemed to be σ-covalent types. Besides iron(II) and iron(III), titanium(IV), chromium(II), cobalt(II), nickel(II), and copper(I) appear to form complexes of the sandwich or half-sandwich type. In addition, a wealth of other complexes have been characterized, where benzenoid, olefinic, and acetylenic ligands are substituted for the cyclopentadienyl group. Although none of these compounds has attained the chemical versatility of ferrocene, and many decompose in attempted organic reactions on the ligands, they are of extraordinary interest for their role in important industrial catalytic processes.[16]

Organosilanes

The lessened polarity of the carbon-silicon bond and the absence of low-lying *p*-orbitals make organosilanes fairly impervious to oxidative or thermal cleavage and much less prone to hydrolytic scission. Similar to the ferrocene nucleus, this integrity of the carbon-silicon molecular skeleton permits many types of organic reactions to be performed. An appealing outcome, then, is that the behavior and the reactivity of organic functional groups can be studied to shed light on the electronic and steric characteristics of a proximate carbon-silicon bond. Within limits, such insights should be important in understanding alkyls of other Group IVA and Group VA metalloids, as well as carbon-metal bonding in general.

In addition, organosilanes have earned much attention as analogs of purely organic compounds, with an eye to assessing how parallel the behavior of carbon and silicon would be. The latter interest found its pioneering proponent in F. S. Kipping, who devoted a lifetime to this quest for analogy, only to conclude that "Even after a very short experience, it was evident that corresponding derivatives of the two elements in question showed very considerable differences in their chemical properties."[17] Thus, being the focus of both inorganic and organic chemists, a formidable body of data has been reported and interrelated. Although tomes would be needed for a complete treatment, the chemistry of organosilanes offers certain particularly salient features worthy of comment in this brief section.[18]

Considered as a metal with dampened traits, silicon forms bonds to carbon that are less polar than those of Groups IA–IIIA (12% ionic character) but those to hydrogen still are reminiscent of metal hydrides. For organosilanes only the tetracovalent disposition of groups about the metalloid center is

[16] (a) G. Wilke, *Angew. Chem.*, **75**, 10 (1963); (b) G. N. Schrauzer, *ibid.*, **76**, 28 (1964).

[17] F. S. Kipping, *Proc. Roy. Soc. (London)*, **159A**, 132 (1937).

[18] C. Eaborn, *Organosilicon Compounds*, Academic, New York, 1960.

known. And in these structures steric access to silicon, compared with the central carbon in tetrasubstituted methanes, is facilitated by the increased covalent radius (Si, 1.13 Å vs. C, 0.77 Å). Although silicon has no available $3s$- or $3p$-orbitals and hence organosilanes form no coordination compounds, it might be noted that highly electronegative ligands permit the attainment of higher coordination numbers

$$SiF_6{}^{--} \quad \text{and} \quad (-O-C=CH-C=O)_3Si^{+}$$
$$\overset{|}{CH_3} \quad \overset{|}{CH_3}$$

apparently by $3sp^3d^2$ hybridization.

From the foregoing, it might be concluded that silicon in organosilanes would behave as a mildly electron-releasing group toward adjacent electronegative elements (C, O, N, Cl). Nevertheless, a substantial body of evidence indicates that the silicon center behaves as an electron-withdrawing group in certain physical and chemical changes. Since silicon is prone to nucleophilic attack (OH⁻, R⁻, NH$_2$⁻), perhaps the electron-withdrawing property of silicon can be viewed as an intramolecular nucleophilic interaction. There is considerable controversy as to whether certain experimental findings are due to the heightened polarity of the silicon (compared to its carbon counterpart) or whether the empty $3d$-orbitals of silicon actually participate in $d_\pi-p_\pi$ bonding with adjacent unshared or π-electrons (V)[19]:

$$R_3Si-\overset{..}{\underset{..}{E}}: \quad \leftrightarrow \quad R_3Si\overset{-}{=}\overset{+.}{\underset{.}{E}}: \quad E = O^-, NR_2^-, C=C$$
$$V$$

Physical measurements of the following types are interpretable in terms of such polar or $d_\pi-p_\pi$ effects[18]: (a) the shorter bond lengths of Si—Cl linkages, the trigonal coplanarity of (H$_3$Si)$_3$N, and the collinearity of Si, N, C, and S in H$_3$SiNCS; (b) the greater acidity of (CH$_3$)$_3$SiOH and the weaker basicity of (H$_3$Si)$_3$N, compared with t-butyl alcohol and trimethylamine, respectively; and (c) the apparent change in the contribution of the normally electron-donating (CH$_3$)$_3$Si group to the dipole moment of p-disubstituted benzenes, (CH$_3$)$_3$Si—C$_6$H$_4$—Z. In the latter dipole moment measurements, the (CH$_3$)$_3$Si group behaves increasingly as an electron acceptor when Z becomes progressively, CH$_3$, NH$_2$, and N(CH$_3$)$_2$. The increasing importance of $d_\pi-p_\pi$ interactions would be consonant with these observations (VI):

[19] D. Seyferth in *Progress in Inorganic Chemistry*, Vol. 3 (F. A. Cotton, ed.), Wiley (Interscience), New York, 1962, Chap. 3.

$$(CH_3)_3Si-\langle\bigcirc\rangle-Z \quad\longleftrightarrow\quad (CH_3)_3Si=\langle\bigcirc\rangle=\overset{\oplus}{Z}$$

VI

The chemical behavior of aryl- and vinyl-silanes often has been interpreted in terms of such d_π—p_π interactions, although another explanation sees such reactions as occurring so as to avoid the increase of positive charge (or to promote the increase of negative charge) next to the pseudocationic silicon. The latter view stresses electrostatic considerations, whereas the d_π—p_π effect emphasizes π-electron density and polarizability. Before a clear choice can be entertained, much more will have to be learned about the detailed mechanisms of the reactions involved. Let us consider what some of these processes are. The addition of hydrogen halides (in the absence of peroxides),[20] of organolithium reagents,[21] and of Group III hydrides (B_2H_6[22] or (i-$C_4H_9)_2AlH$)[23] to $R_3SiCH=CH_2$ yields as the principal product that adduct placing the electropositive group M (H, Li, and Al) on the carbon adjacent to silicon (VII). Steric factors cannot be the sole determining consideration, since

M
|
$R_3Si-C-CH_3$
|
H

VII

H H
| |
$R_3Si-C-C-M$
| |
H H

VIII

even with diisobutylaluminum hydride the major product (70%) is still VII [M = $(C_4H_9)_2Al$]. The more attractive product sterically, VIII, is formed in only 30% yield. If such hydride additions be viewed as electrophilic attack by MH_3, then attack at the *alpha* carbon of the vinyl group suggests a lower activation energy because of greater electron availability in the transition state (cf. IX–XI).

$$\left[\begin{matrix} R_3Si \\ \\ H \end{matrix}\!\!\underset{\underset{\ominus}{R_2'Al-H}}{\overset{}{\searrow}}\!\!\overset{\oplus}{C}-CH_2\right] \xleftarrow{R_2'Al-H} \begin{matrix} R_3Si-CH=CH_2 \\ \uparrow \\ \downarrow \\ R_3Si-\overset{-}{CH}-\overset{+}{CH_2} \end{matrix} \xrightarrow{R_2'Al-H} \left[\begin{matrix} R_3Si \\ \\ H \end{matrix}\!\!\underset{\underset{\ominus}{H-AlR_2'}}{\overset{}{\searrow}}\!\!\overset{\oplus}{C}-CH_2\right]$$

IX   X   XI

[20] L. H. Sommer, G. M. Goldberg, C. E. Buck, T. S. Bye, F. J. Evans, and F. C. Whitmore, *J. Am. Chem. Soc.*, **76**, 1613 (1954).
[21] L. F. Cason and H. G. Brooks, *J. Am. Chem. Soc.*, **74**, 4582 (1952).
[22] D. Seyferth, *J. Am. Chem. Soc.*, **81**, 1844 (1959).
[23] J. J. Eisch and G. R. Husk, *J. Org. Chem.*, **29**, 254 (1964).

Further physical evidence, such as correlations of *trans*-vinylic hydrogen n.m.r. chemical shifts[24] and of vinylic CH_2[25] out-of-plane deformation with Hammett parameters for the system, $R_3Si-CH=CH_2$, is in excellent agreement with the operation of a $d_\pi-p_\pi$ effect in the equilibrated molecules. And, finally, the arresting observation that vinylsilanes can undergo bimolecular reductive coupling with lithium is very reminiscent of the behavior of conjugated dienes[26]:

$$2(C_6H_5)_3Si-CH=CH_2 \xrightarrow{\text{Li/THF}} 2(C_6H_5)_3Si-\overset{-}{C}H-\overset{\cdot}{C}H_2 \longrightarrow \begin{array}{c} (C_6H_5)_3Si-\overset{-}{C}H-CH_2 \\ | \\ (C_6H_5)_3Si-\overset{-}{C}H-CH_2 \end{array}$$

$$(8\text{--}14)$$

In the foregoing brief description, emphasis has been placed upon the study of the carbon-silicon bond as a muted type of carbon-metal bond. From another viewpoint, it is of interest to assess silicon as a carbon analog and hence to learn whether silicon-metal bonds resemble carbon-metal linkages. Fascinating are the reversals in expected behavior, when triphenylsilylmetallics and triphenylmethylmetallics are compared. The former is by far the stronger base and more reactive nucleophile, as the following examples bear out[27]:

$$(C_6H_5)_3SiK \begin{cases} \xrightarrow{(C_6H_5)_3CH} (C_6H_5)_3SiH + (C_6H_5)_3CK & (8\text{--}15) \\ \xrightarrow{C_6H_5Br} (C_6H_5)_4Si & (8\text{--}16) \\ \xrightarrow{CO_2} (C_6H_5)_3Si-\overset{O}{\overset{\|}{C}}-OH & (8\text{--}17) \end{cases}$$

Moreover, triphenylsilylmetallics add to C=C, C=O, and C=N linkages, which are responsive to RLi types, but not to $(C_6H_5)_3CLi$. An intriguing rearrangement (the reverse of the Wittig rearrangement for ordinary organometallics) often is a sequel to the usual mode of addition:

$$(C_6H_5)_3SiLi + (C_6H_5)_2C=O \rightarrow (C_6H_5)_3Si-\overset{OLi}{\overset{|}{C}}(C_6H_5)_2 \xrightarrow{\Delta} (C_6H_5)_3SiO\overset{Li}{\overset{|}{C}}(C_6H_5)_2 \quad (8\text{--}18)$$

$$(C_6H_5)_3SiK + (C_6H_5)_2C=N-C_6H_5 \longrightarrow (C_6H_5)_3Si(C_6H_5)_2C-NKC_6H_5$$

$$\xrightarrow[H_2O]{\Delta} (C_6H_5)_2CH-N(C_6H_5)Si(C_6H_5)_3 \quad (8\text{--}19)$$

[24] R. Summitt, J. J. Eisch, J. T. Trainor, and M. T. Rogers, *J. Phys. Chem.*, **67**, 2362 (1963).
[25] J. J. Eisch and J. T. Trainor, *J. Org. Chem.*, **28**, 487 (1963).
[26] J. J. Eisch and R. J. Beuhler, *J. Org. Chem.*, **28**, 2876 (1963).
[27] D. Wittenberg and H. Gilman, *Quart. Rev.* (*London*), **13**, 116 (1959).

$$(C_6H_5)_3SiLi + R_2NH \rightarrow (C_6H_5)_3SiH + R_2NLi \rightarrow LiH + (C_6H_5)_3Si—NR_2 \quad (8\text{-}20)$$

$$(C_6H_5)_3SiLi \xrightarrow[\text{2. } H_2O]{\text{1. } CO_2} (C_6H_5)_3Si—\overset{\displaystyle O}{\overset{\displaystyle \parallel}{C}}—OH \longrightarrow (C_6H_5)_3Si—OH + CO\uparrow \quad (8\text{-}21)$$

The synthesis of functionally substituted organosilanes via these silyl-metallics is clearly an extraordinarily versatile route. In addition, the greater resistance of carbon-silicon bonds to oxidative and hydrolytic cleavage permits the preparation of numerous organosilane derivatives by the application of straightforward organic reactions to certain key organosilanes. Some of the

CHART 8–2

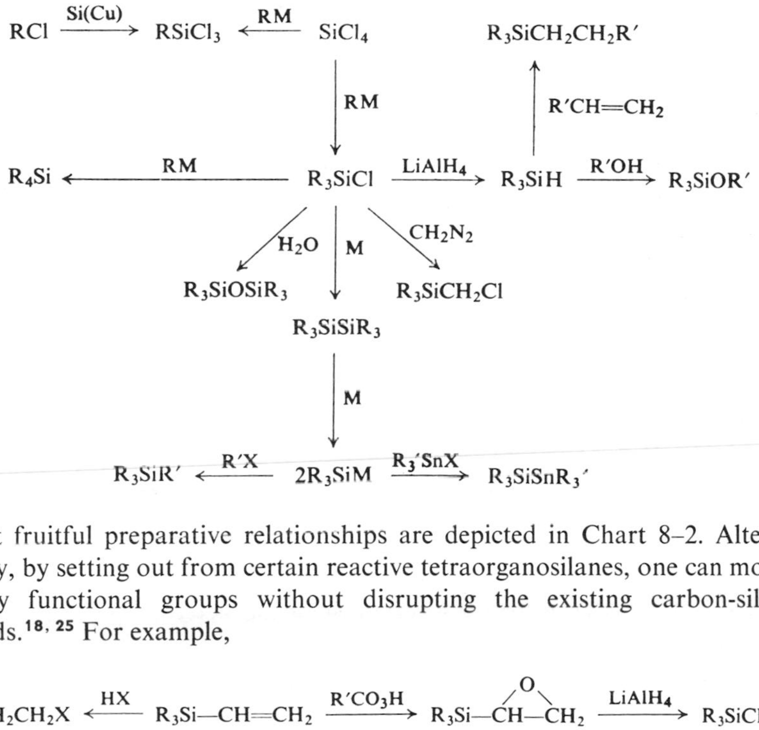

most fruitful preparative relationships are depicted in Chart 8–2. Alternatively, by setting out from certain reactive tetraorganosilanes, one can modify many functional groups without disrupting the existing carbon-silicon bonds.[18, 25] For example,

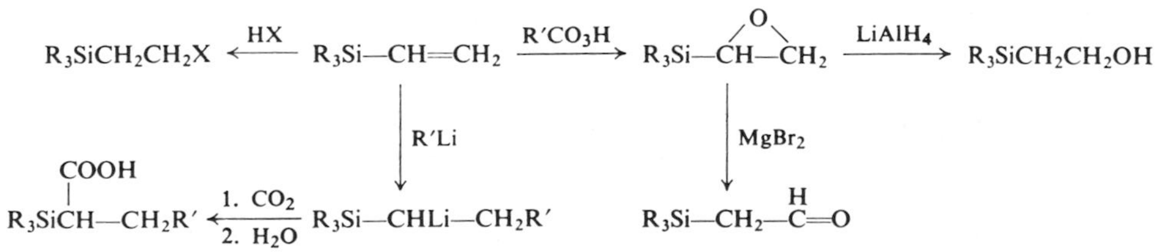

Not only do the foregoing reactions demonstrate the existence and accessibility of a wide variety of organosilanes, but present research gives witness to a growing intensity in mechanistic studies. The superb research on

the stereochemistry of reactions at asymmetric silicon promises to lend insight into many substitution processes.[28] The unresolved question as to whether p_π—p_π bonds to silicon have any reality, as well as the related problem of d_π—p_π bonding is receiving quickening attention. Finally, the concatenating ability of silicon atoms, giving rise to silicon chains and rings, is of obvious interest in regard to problems of conformation and chain aggregation in polysilanes.[29]

Aromatic Organometallic Heterocycles

In formal adherence to the Hückel rule for aromaticity, these aromatic systems would be composed of a monocyclic planar array of atoms each of which possesses a *p*-orbital of the right geometry which is not involved in a σ-bond. Although each atomic *p*-orbital may contribute 0, 1, or 2 electrons to the π-molecular orbital, the sum of π-electrons shall be $4n + 2$.[30] In actual practice, the necessary planarity is most dependent upon the ring size and the effective conjugation of *p*-orbitals is sensitive to their relative energies and overlap integrals. Since a confident prediction of π-electron stabilization energies (aromatic resonance energies) is not possible at present, a synthetic chemist need have few inhibitions in attempting ingenious approaches to candidate rings. The further participation of metals in cyclic conjugation by virtue of their *d*-orbitals has been suggested; in which case d_π—p_π conjugation is considered to establish aromatic delocalization. *A priori*, then, metals such as boron, aluminum, gallium, silicon, germanium, phosphorus, arsenic, and certain transition metals might yield cyclic conjugated systems. What criteria should be used in establishing aromatic character is less certain. Surely one should not expect a complete disappearance of the usual carbon-metal bond character. Hence, oxidative or hydrolytic stability may not be outstanding. Physical measurements should prove a more reliable hallmark of aromaticity: (a) ultraviolet evidence for conjugation involving heteroatoms; (b) nuclear magnetic resonance spectral evidence for ring currents causing vinyl proton deshielding and signal degeneracy; (c) X-ray crystallographic evidence of bond length adjustments; and (d) nuclear quadrupole or Mössbauer spectroscopic evidence for metal hybridization and oxidation state. In sum, then, the study of potentially conjugated heterocycles of well-defined geometry provides an excellent model for evaluating hybridization states of carbon-

---

[28] L. H. Sommer, K. W. Michael, and W. D. Korte, *J. Am. Chem. Soc.*, **85**, 3712 (1963).

[29] H. Gilman and G. L. Schwebke, in *Advances in Organometallic Chemistry*, Vol. 1 (F. G. A. Stone and R. West, eds.), Academic, New York, 1964, Chap. 3.

[30] A. Streitwieser, Jr., *Molecular Orbital Theory for Organic Chemists*, Wiley, New York, 1962, Chap. 10.

metal σ-bonds, as well as the relative importance of carbon-metal π-bonds (p_π—p_π, d_π—p_π, or d_π—d_π interactions).

It is natural that the preparation of organometallic heterocycles will encompass more than just Hückel aromatic systems. For a corollary of aromatic character is that systems bearing $4n$ π-electrons should not attain the same chemical or physical levels of stability. Hence the general synthetic goal is that of preparing various types of unsaturated rings, in order to discover the effect of ring size and nature of ring atoms on the stability and on the chemical and physical properties. An instructive selection of metallocyclic syntheses is presented in the following equations:

(1) The condensation of a metal halide with a hydrogen derivative of a nonmetal:

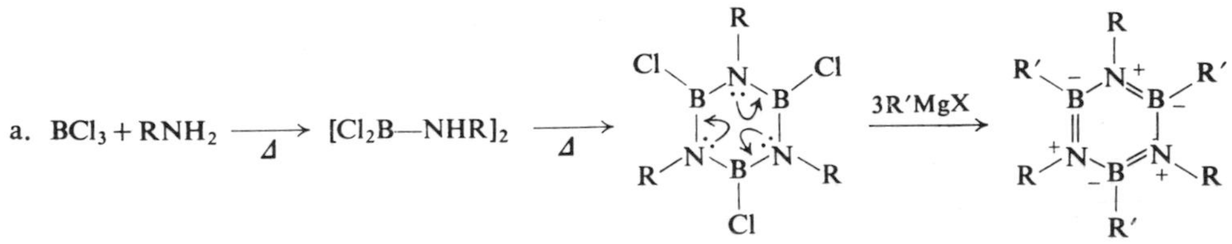

a. $BCl_3 + RNH_2 \xrightarrow{\Delta} [Cl_2B-NHR]_2 \xrightarrow{\Delta}$

$$\xrightarrow{3R'MgX}$$

(8–22)[31]

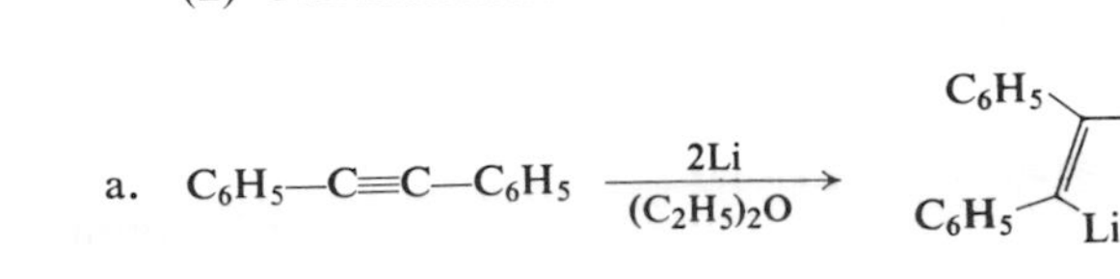

b.

$$\xrightarrow[AlCl_3]{AsCl_3}$$

(8–23)[32]

(2) The interaction of the desired metal halide with a dimetallo derivative:

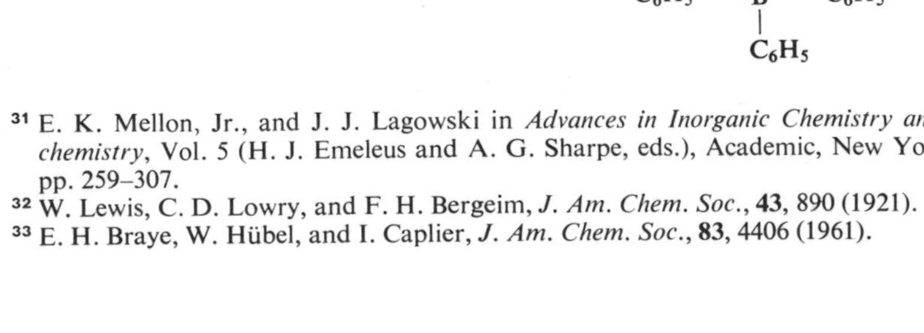

a. $C_6H_5-C\equiv C-C_6H_5 \xrightarrow[(C_2H_5)_2O]{2Li}$

$$\xrightarrow{C_6H_5BCl_2}$$

(8–24)[33]

[31] E. K. Mellon, Jr., and J. J. Lagowski in *Advances in Inorganic Chemistry and Radiochemistry*, Vol. 5 (H. J. Emeleus and A. G. Sharpe, eds.), Academic, New York, 1963, pp. 259–307.

[32] W. Lewis, C. D. Lowry, and F. H. Bergeim, *J. Am. Chem. Soc.*, **43**, 890 (1921).

[33] E. H. Braye, W. Hübel, and I. Caplier, *J. Am. Chem. Soc.*, **83**, 4406 (1961).

b.

$$(8-25)^{34}$$

(3) Cyclization by intramolecular metalation:

a.

$$(8-26)^{35}$$

b.

$$(8-27)^{36}$$

[34] H. Gilman and E. A. Zuech, *J. Org. Chem.*, **27**, 2897 (1962).
[35] J. J. Eisch and W. C. Kaska, *J. Am. Chem. Soc.*, **84**, 1501 (1962).
[36] J. J. Eisch and M. E. Healy, *J. Am. Chem. Soc.*, **86**, 4221 (1964).

(4) Additions with compounds of metals in lower oxidation states:

a. $2C_6H_5-C\equiv C-C_6H_5 \xrightarrow{GeI_2}$ $(8-28)^{37}$

b. $2C_6H_5-C\equiv C-C_6H_5 \xrightarrow{Fe_3(CO)_{12}}$ $(8-29)^{38}$

c. $C_6H_5-C\equiv C-C_6H_5 \xrightarrow{Pt(P(C_6H_5)_3)_2}$ $(8-30)^{39}$

(5) Di-addition of metal hydrides to unsaturates:

a. $\xrightarrow{RBH_2 \cdot N(CH_3)_3}$ $(8-31)^{40}$

b. $C_6H_5-C\equiv C-H \xrightarrow{(C_6H_5)_2SnH_2}$ $(8-32)^{41}$

[37] (a) M. E. Volpin, Y. D. Koreshkov, V. G. Dulova, and D. N. Kursanov, *Tetrahedron*, **18**, 107 (1962); (b) F. Johnson and R. S. Gohlke, XIX International Congress, IUPAC, July 1963, Abstracts of Organic Chemistry, p. 163, Butterworths, London.
[38] W. Hübel and E. H. Braye, *J. Inorg. Nucl. Chem.*, **10**, 250 (1959).
[39] J. Chatt, G. A. Rowe, and A. A. Williams, *Proc. Chem. Soc.*, **1957**, 208.
[40] M. F. Hawthorne, *J. Am. Chem. Soc.*, **82**, 748 (1960); **83**, 2541 (1961).
[41] M. C. Henry and J. G. Noltes, *J. Am. Chem. Soc.*, **82**, 561 (1960).

(6) Organic transformations of saturated heterocycles:

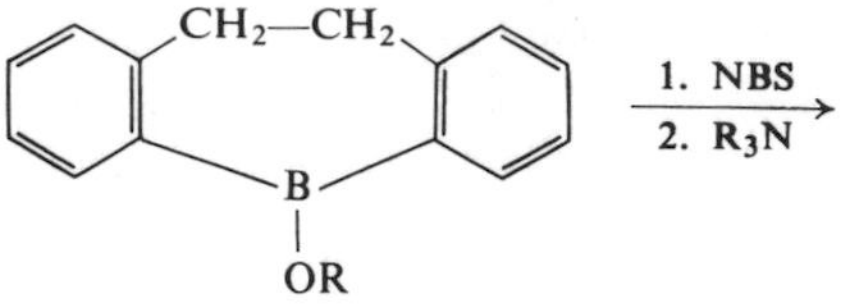

$$(8\text{-}33)\,[42]$$

The most abundant evidence bearing on the question of aromaticity with such systems stems from research with boron-nitrogen heterocycles. The properties of the borazole or borazine system are most informative. Extensive research by Stock,[43] Schlesinger,[44] G. F. Schaeffer,[45] and others have uncovered marked parallelisms between their physical properties (colligative phenomena, bond distances, ultraviolet spectra) and those of the corresponding aromatic derivative:

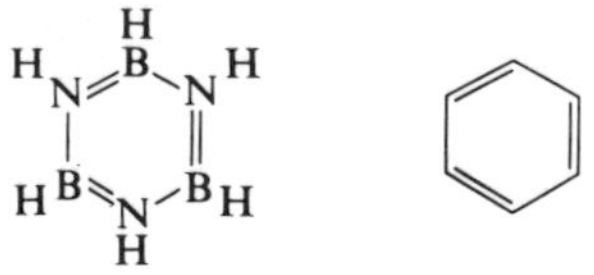

b.p., °K	328	353
m.p., °K	215	279
molar volume at b.p., °K	99.42	96.42
molar polarization, cm³	24	27
ring atom separation, Å	1.44	1.42

Recently, Dewar and coworkers have devoted much attention to the synthesis and properties of the partially carbocyclic borazarenes.[46] For example, 10,9-borazarophenanthrenes possess sufficient chemical stability to permit their ultraviolet examination in ethanol and study of their behavior upon electrophilic substitution[47]:

[42] E. E. van Tamelen, G. Brieger, and K. G. Untch, *Tetrahedron Letters*, **1960** (8), 14.
[43] A. Stock and E. Pohland, *Ber.*, **59**, 2215 (1926).
[44] H. Schlesinger et al., *J. Am. Chem. Soc.*, **58**, 409 (1936); **60**, 1296 (1938).
[45] G. W. Schaeffer et al., *J. Am. Chem. Soc.*, **71**, 2143 (1949); **73**, 1612 (1951).
[46] M. J. S. Dewar, G. J. Gleicher, and B. P. Robinson, *J. Am. Chem. Soc.*, **86**, 5698 (1964).
[47] M. J. S. Dewar and V. P. Kubba, *Tetrahedron*, **7**, 213 (1959).

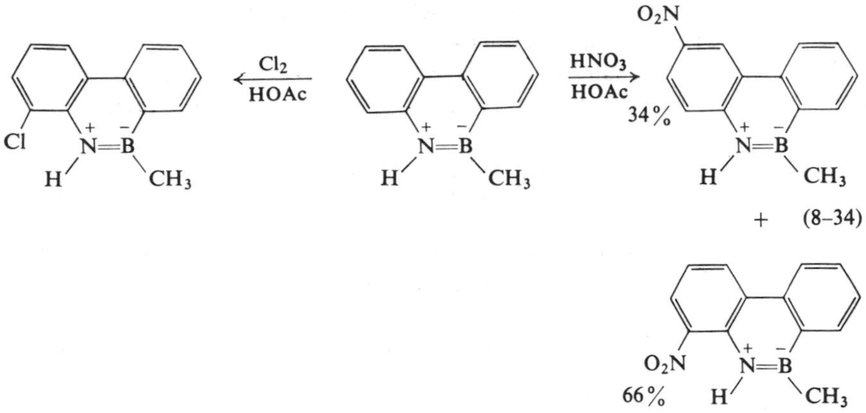

$$+ \quad (8\text{–}34)$$

Metal–Metal Bonding

Either in the structure of metal-atom chains or rings in certain organo-metalloids, $[(C_6H_5)_2Sn]_n$, or in an understanding of organoidal-metallic compounds, the question of the nature of metal-metal bonding arises. Clearly, two important types can be distinguished: homopolar bonding between metals of very similar electronegativities, typified by R_3Si—SiR_3, R_3Sn—PbR_3, and R_2As—AsR_2; and heteropolar bonding between very dissimilar metals, as for example, $(C_6H_5)_3SiK$, $(CO)_4CoNa$, and $(C_6H_5)_2PLi$. Bond energy estimates for many types of such bonds are unavailable, but certain trends are noteworthy. Homopolar bonds between atoms of Group I are relatively weak (Li—Li, 25; Na—Na, 17.3; K—K, 11.8; Rb—Rb, 10.8; Cs—Cs, 10.4 kcal/mole); but such bonds among Groups IV, V and VI atoms are considerably stronger (C—Si, 57.6; Si—Si, 42.5; Ge—Ge, 42.5; Se—Se, 57.6). Consequently, elemental concatenation tends to be optimized among the metalloids and nonmetals. Polyorganosilanes containing at least nine silicons in a chain or six silicons in a ring have been characterized. Similar examples have been reported for germanium(XII)[48] and tin(XIII)[49] systems:

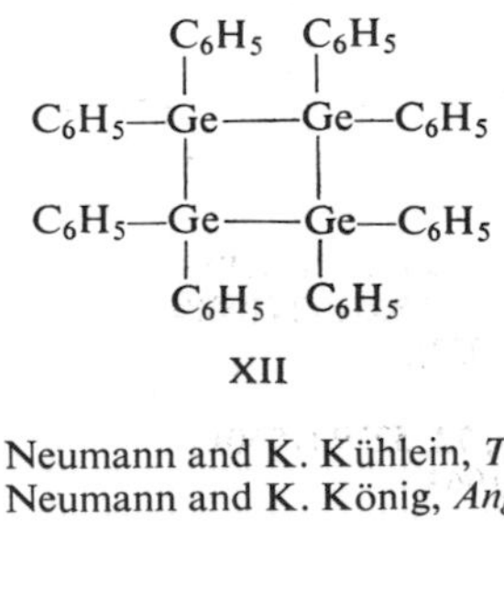

XII

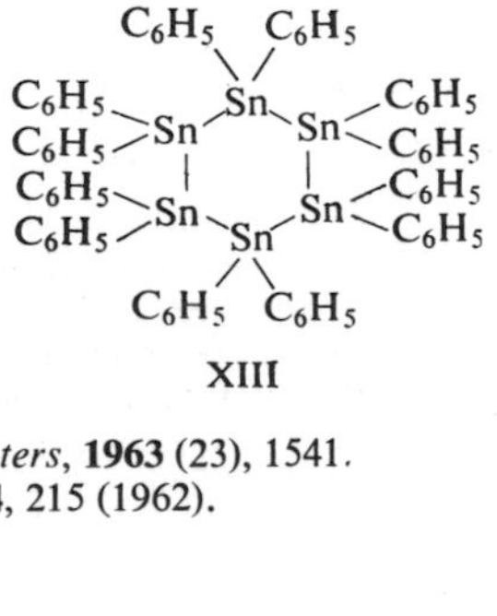

XIII

[48] W. P. Neumann and K. Kühlein, *Tetrahedron Letters*, **1963** (23), 1541.
[49] W. P. Neumann and K. König, *Angew. Chem.*, **74**, 215 (1962).

The foregoing homopolar metal-metal bonds are related to heteropolar linkages by certain chemical transformations which serve as the usual synthetic approaches to such linkages. First, homopolar bonds can usually be cleaved to heteropolar bonds by alkali metal under appropriate conditions[50]:

$$R_nM—MR_n \xrightarrow[\text{donor solvent}]{\text{Na}} 2R_nM—Na \qquad (8\text{-}35)$$

Second, heteropolar bonds usually give way to homopolar bonds (or heteropolar bonds of lower polarity) by treatment with metallic halides[50]:

$$R_nM—Na + X—MR_n \to R_nM—MR_n + NaX \qquad (8\text{-}36)$$

The reactivity and versatility of heteropolar metal-metal bonds is the reason why organoidal-metallic reagents $[(C_6H_5)_3SiK, (C_6H_5)_2PLi)]$ have such great synthetic appeal (cf. section on *Organosilanes*). The following examples amplify this point:

$$(CO)_4CoNa \xrightarrow{\text{CH}_3\text{I}} (CO)_4Co—CH_3 \qquad (8\text{-}37)^{[51]}$$

$$(C_6H_5)_3SiK \xrightarrow{(C_6H_5)_3SnCl} (C_6H_5)_3Si—Sn(C_6H_5)_3 \qquad (8\text{-}38)^{[52]}$$

$$(C_6H_5)_2PLi \xrightarrow{(C_6H_5C\equiv C—Cl)} (C_6H_5)_2P—C\equiv CC_6H_5 \qquad (8\text{-}39)^{[53]}$$

$$(C_6H_5)_3GeNa \xrightarrow{\text{Cl}_3\text{SiH}} [(C_6H_5)_3Ge]_3SiH \qquad (8\text{-}40)^{[54]}$$

It is almost inevitable that homopolar organometallics, having weak metal-metal bonds, would be difficult to prepare. Attractive modes of decomposition, disproportionation and rearrangement, may be the basis for past failures;[55] for example:

$$(C_6H_5)_2AlCl \xrightarrow{\text{Na}} [2(C_6H_5)_2Al\cdot \rightleftharpoons (C_6H_5)_2Al—Al(C_6H_5)_2]$$

$$\longrightarrow (C_6H_5)_3Al + Al \xrightarrow{\text{Na}} C_6H_5Na + Al \qquad (8\text{-}41)$$

However, the existence of diboron tetrachloride and its interesting chemistry encourages the hope that other organometallic examples of such systems may

[50] D. Wittenberg and H. Gilman, *Quart. Rev. (London)*, **13**, 116 (1959).
[51] W. Hieber, O. Vohler, and G. Braun, *Z. Naturforsch.*, **136**, 192 (1958).
[52] H. Gilman and T. C. Wu, *J. Org. Chem.*, **18**, 753 (1953).
[53] K. Issleib and G. Harzfeld, *Ber.*, **95**, 268 (1962).
[54] J. G. Milligan and C. A. Kraus, *J. Am. Chem. Soc.*, **72**, 5279 (1950).
[55] J. J. Eisch and W. C. Kaska, unpublished studies, 1963.

be synthesized and that they may add to carbon-carbon unsaturation with interesting consequences[56]:

$$(8\text{-}42)$$

Not only does much synthetic work remain to be done in this area, but the electronic properties of these metal-metal bonds present an attractive object for future kinetic and thermodynamic investigation. Largely unresolved are such questions as whether bond cleavage occurs homolytically or hetero-lytically in individual reactions, whether 1,2- or 1,4-additions to conjugated organic systems occur, and what the electron-transmitting properties (induction or resonance) of such bonds are.[57]

$$(8\text{-}43)$$

In terms of Rundle's fruitful suggestion that the bonding in associated metal alkyls is reminiscent of delocalized bonding in metals themselves, further insight gained from a study of metal-metal or metalloid-metalloid bonding in organometallics may shed light on the electronic properties of the metal state itself.[58]

[56] W. B. Fox and T. Wartik, *J. Am. Chem. Soc.*, **83**, 498 (1961).
[57] (a) D. N. Hagur, *Proc. Chem. Soc.*, **1962**, 300; (b) R. Waack and M. A. Doran, *Chem. Ind.* (*London*), **1965**, 563.
[58] R. E. Rundle, *J. Phys. Chem.*, **61**, 45 (1957).

NINE
Conclusion

An organic chemist's interest in organometallic compounds leads into research areas and produces chemical insights scarcely imagined at the outset. The Nobel laureate, Professor Karl Ziegler, has expressed admirably the inexorable and inseparable series of observations and further experimentation leading up to his fundamental discoveries in organoaluminum chemistry.[1] The research in this field prompts excursions into the realms of inorganic and physical and polymer chemistry, with little regard for the traditional areas of chemical specialization. Further, organometallic chemistry with its emphasis on substances foreign to natural products, probably has revitalized organic chemistry at mid-century. However, it may turn out that the organometallic chemistry of transition metals may furnish unexpected information on the role of metals in biochemical processes. Thus, though the organometallic world of moisture- and oxygen-sensitive substances has seemed totally irrelevant to the world of life processes, future chemists may be amused by this view. Only recently Schrauzer and coworkers have synthesized organocobalt models of vitamin B_{12} derivatives and have found these model compounds to possess marked similarities to naturally occurring coenzymes.[2]

[1] (a) K. Ziegler, *Glueckauf*, **91**, 1 (1955); (b) K. Ziegler, *Experientia Suppl.*, **2**, 274 (1955); XIV IUPAC meeting, Zürich, July 1955.

[2] G. N. Schrauzer, R. J. Windgassen, J. Kohnle, and G. Kratel, *Abstracts of Proceedings, 2nd International Symposium on Organometallic Chemistry*, Madison, Wis., Aug. 30–Sept. 3, 1965.

Finally, because of the abundance and distribution of metals in the universe, it is difficult to comprehend all the implications of organometallic chemistry to the possible evolution of compounds and life as we know it. Occurrence of metallic carbides, hydrogen, nitrogen, methane, and water on the primordial earth might have set the stage for reactions that were prototypes of the oxo, Haber, Reppe, and Ziegler processes. In this manner a large pool of simple organic molecules might have arisen at low temperatures during the eons before life emerged.[3] The researcher in organometallic chemistry thus empathizes with Wagner in Goethe's *Faust* who declares:

> Mit Eifer hab ich mich der Studien beflissen;
> Zwar weiss ich viel, doch möcht ich alles wissen.[4]

Although future research may not equal Wagner's success in synthesizing a "glass-enclosed manikin," one senses that organometallic catalysis may yet put enzyme research onto rich trails of success.

---

[3] H. C. Urey, *The Planets, their Origin and Development*, Yale University Press, New Haven, Conn., 1952, p. 245.

[4] J. W. v. Goethe, *Faust*, First Part, Act 1: "My studies I have with ardor pursued; Full of lore, I burn to have all accrued."

APPENDIX
Bibliography

Coates, G. E., *Organometallic Compounds*, 2nd ed., Wiley, New York, 1960. An outstanding factual account of the preparation and properties of organometallic compounds, arranged according to periodic families.

Cotton, F. A., and G. Wilkinson, *Advanced Inorganic Chemistry*, Wiley, New York, 1962. Thoroughly modern correlation of chemical bonding with molecular properties, together with many structural illustrations drawn from organometallic chemistry.

Eisch, J., and H. Gilman, in Organometallic Compounds in *Advances in Inorganic Chemistry and Radiochemistry*, Vol. 2 (H. J. Emeleus and A. G. Sharpe, eds.), Academic, New York, 1960. A review of research trends and significant findings.

Harwood, J. H., *Industrial Applications of Organometallic Compounds*, Reinhold, New York, 1963.

Kharasch, M. S., and O. Reinmuth, *Grignard Reactions of Nonmetallic Substances*, Prentice-Hall, Englewood Cliffs, N.J., 1954. A classic compilation and commentary on the organic chemistry of organomagnesium compounds.

King, R. B., and J. J. Eisch (eds.), *Organometallic Synthesis*, Vols. 1–2, Academic, New York, 1965. A compilation of reliable preparative procedures and a discussion of specialized technique.

Krause, E., and A. von Grosse, *Die Chemie der metall-organischen Verbindungen*, Borntraeger, Berlin, 1937. First exhaustive and systematic treatment of organometallics, which has become the *vade mecum* of all researchers.

Rochow, E. G., D. J. Hurd, and R. N. Lewis, *The Chemistry of Organometallic Compounds*, Wiley, New York, 1957. An excellent presentation of the preparation and properties of metal alkyls based upon a periodic table grouping of metals.

164

Stone, F. G. A., and R. West, *Advances in Organometallic Chemistry*, Vols. 1–2, Academic, New York, 1964.

Zeiss, H. (ed.), *Organometallic Chemistry*, Reinhold, New York, 1960. Detailed presentations of frontiers in organometallic research by those investigators in the vanguard.

Journal of Organometallic Chemistry, Vols. 1–3, Elsevier, Amsterdam, 1963.

Index